BMA's
Question Papers
for Science & Maths
Olympiads & Talent Exams

Class 6

Brain Mapping Academy

Published by:

Brain Mapping Academy
#16-11-16/1/B, First Floor, Farhath Hospital Road,
Saleem Nagar, Malakpet, Hyderabad-500 036.
✆ 040-66135169, 65165169.
E-mail: info@bmatalent.com
Website: www.bmatalent.com

© **BRAIN MAPPING ACADEMY**
ALL RIGHTS RESERVED
No part of this book may be reproduced, stored in a retrieval system or transmitted in any form or by any means, electronic, mechanical, photocopying, recording or otherwise without the prior written permission of the publisher.

ISBN : 978-9380299-61-7

Disclaimer
Every care has been taken by the compilers and publishers to give correct, complete and updated information. In case there is any omission, printing mistake or any other error which might have crept in inadvertently, neither the compiler / publisher nor any of the distributors take any legal responsibility.

In case of any dispute, all matters are subjected to the exclusive jurisdiction of the courts in Hyderabad only.

Printed at:
Sri Vinayaka Art Printers, Hyderabad.

CONTENTS

Model Paper - 1 1–16

Model Paper - 2 17–34

Model Paper - 3 35–54

NSTSE – 2011 55–83

Key 84

CLASS: VI Brain Mapping Academy

CLASS: VI Model Paper - 1 MATHEMATICS

1. In the figure below, points A, O and C lie on the same line.

   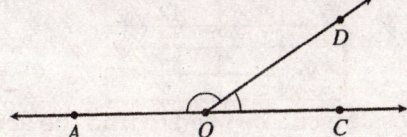

   What is the sum of the measures of angle AOD and angle DOC ?

   (A) 90^0 (B) 180^0 (C) 270^0 (D) 360^0

2. At Vivek's school there is 1 teacher for every 15 students. There are 630 students at the school. Which proportion can be used to find x the number of teachers ?

   (A) $\dfrac{x}{15} = \dfrac{1}{630}$ (B) $\dfrac{15}{1} = \dfrac{x}{630}$ (C) $\dfrac{1}{15} = \dfrac{x}{630}$ (D) $\dfrac{x}{1} = \dfrac{15}{615}$

3. Alekya is baking cookies for 16 children. She has baked 2 dozen cookies. If she wants each child to receive exactly 2 cookies and have no cookies left over, how many more cookies should she bake ?

   (A) 1.5   (B) 8   (C) 24   (D) 32

4. Kamali knows the circumference of her bicycle tyre, but she needs to find the diameter.

   Which method can Kamali use to find the diameter ?
   (A) Multiply the circumference by 2 and divide the result by π
   (B) Divide the circumference by 2 and multiply the result by π
   (C) Multiply the circumference by π
   (D) Divide the circumference by π

5. The table below shows the areas of a triangle where the height of the triangle stays the same but the base changes.

Model Paper - 1

Areas of Triangles

Height (Units)	Base (Units)	Area (square units)
6	2	6
6	4	12
6	6	18
6	8	24
6	n	?

Which expression can be used to find the area of a triangle that has a height of 6 units and a base of n units ?

(A) $\dfrac{n}{2}$ (B) $\dfrac{6}{2}$ (C) $\dfrac{6n}{2}$ (D) 6n

6. Which of the following is the least common multiple that Bhargavi can use to add three fractions with denominators of 6,8 and 9 ?

   (A) 48 (B) 54 (C) 72 (D) 144

7. What value of "a" makes the equation below true ?

   $$-12 + (-3(A)) = 0$$

   (A) 5 (B) -4
   (C) 4 (D) -5

8. Roshini is stitching a quilt from square pieces of cloth. The squares form the pattern shown in the diagram.

   Which two squares of cloth should be added to the above diagram so that the pattern will continue ?

   (A)  (B)   (C)   (D)

9. Which of the following, when divided by 5, will always be greater than 5 ?

   (A) All numbers greater than 25 (B) All numbers less than 5
   (C) All numbers between 0 and 10 (D) All numbers between 5 and 25

Model Paper - 1

10. In 1995, the population of Delhi was about 43, 200. In 2005, the population was about 40,100. What was the approximate percent of decrease in population over this ten-year period ?
   (A) 7%   (B) 9%   (C) 31%   (D) 93%
11. In this drawing, line *l* is parallel to line m. The measure of ∠1 is 110 degrees. What is the measure of ∠2 ?

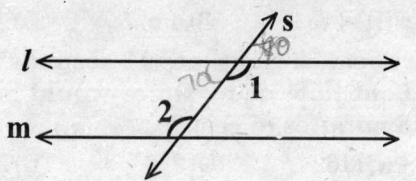

   (A) 40°   (B) 55°   (C) 70°   (D) 110°
12. One number is 5 less than four times another. If their sum is 55, then find the largest number out of those two numbers ?
   (A) 43   (B) 50   (C) 11   (D) 60
13. 10 men can do a piece of work in 6 days. How long will it take to do the same work for 5 men ?
   (A) 3 days   (B) 6 days   (C) 10 days   (D) 12 days
14. Which of the following pairs is not in proportion ?
   (A) 3 : 2 and 6 : 4   (B) 2 : 3 and 4 : 9
   (C) 5 : 7 and 10 : 14   (D) 6 : 7 and 18 : 21
15. Which of the following number sentences is represented on the number line shown below ?

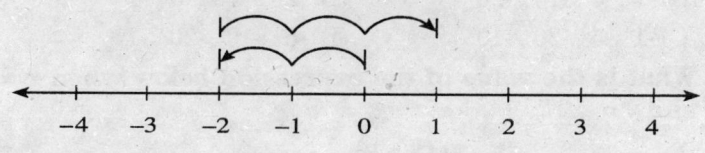

   (A) -2 + (-3) = 1   (B) 1 + (-2) = -2
   (C) 1- (+2) = -1   (D) -2 + 3 = 1
16. A triangle has angles measuring 45° and 55°. What is the measure of the triangle's third angle ?
   (A) 80°   (B) 100°   (C) 125°   (D) 135°

Model Paper - 1

17. During a basket-ball season Nandini made 2 out of every 3 free throws she attempted. In the last basket-ball game, Nandini attempted 12 free throws. How many free throws would she have been expected to make ?
    (A) 2   (B) 8   (C) 24   (D) 36
18. An animal shelter currently has 20 cats and 25 dogs. What is the ratio of cats to dogs ?
    (A) 5 to 4   (B) 4 to 9   (C) 4 to 5   (D) 1 to 5
19. Sonali's heart beats 9 times per 10 seconds while Sonali is resting. About how many times would Sonali's heart beat during 3 minutes of rest ?
    (A) 27   (B) 162   (C) 270   (D) 200
20. Ayesha recorded the daily minimum temperatures as shown in the table.

    Daily Minimum Temperatures

Day	Temperature In Degrees Fahernheit
Monday	-10^0
Tuesday	-5^0
Wednesday	-20^0
Thursday	-1^0

    Which of the following lists the temperatures in order from the LOWEST to the HIGHEST ?
    (A) $-1^0, -5^0, -10^0, -20^0$ (B) $-20^0, -10^0, -5^0, -1^0$
    (C) $-1^0, -5^0, -20^0, -10^0$ (D) $-5^0, -10^0, -20^0, -1^0$
21. What is the value of the expression below when x = 12 and y = -12 ?
    $$(x - y)(x + y)$$
    (A) 288   (B) 144   (C) 12   (D) 0
22. If 7x+3=17, what is the value of 7x-3?
    (A) -3   (B) 0   (C) 11   (D) 14

Model Paper - 1

23. Which of the following numbers is divisible by 2, 4 and 8?

   (A) 9840   (B) 5401   (C) 7834   (D) 4076

24. Choose the correct statement from the following.

   (A) A line has definite length
   (B) A ray has definite length
   (C) A line segment has definite length
   (D) None of these

25. Which of the following can be the remainder when a positive integer is divided by 17 ?

   (A) 71   (B) 12   (C) 19   (D) 17

CLASS: VI — PHYSICS

26. At a particular temperature, the reading is 'X' in Kelvin scale & Y in the Celsius scale. If the temperature increases by 10°C in the Celsius scale, then the new temperature shown in the Kelvin scale will be :

   (A) X + 10   (B) X + 273   (C) X + 373   (D) X – 10

27. Which of the following is the biggest unit of time ?

   (A) Hour   (B) Year   (C) Day   (D) Light year

28. A man has to cover a distance of 200 m. He covers the first 100 m in 3 min 20 sec. He stops for 1min and then covers the next 100m in 4 min. What is his average speed?

   (A) 4 m/s   (B) 0.4 m/s   (C) 28.5 m/s   (D) 0.8 m/s

29. Which of the following cannot be done by the application of force ?

   (A) Stop a moving body.   (B) Change the speed of a moving body.
   (C) Move a body at rest.   (D) Change the mass of a body.

30. The motion of the wheel of a car moving at a constant velocity is:

   (A) translatory & rotatory   (B) rotatory
   (C) translatory, rotatory and periodic   (D) translatory & oscillatory

Model Paper - 1

31. A man is pulled by a force of 490 N by the earth. What is his mass?

    (A) 40 kg   (B) 50 kg   (C) 45 kgf   (D) 49 N

32. The following three units are all related :

    1. N   2. Pa m^2 3. J/m

    They are all :

    (A) units of heat   (B) base units

    (C) units of pressure   (D) units of force

33. Study the figures given below.

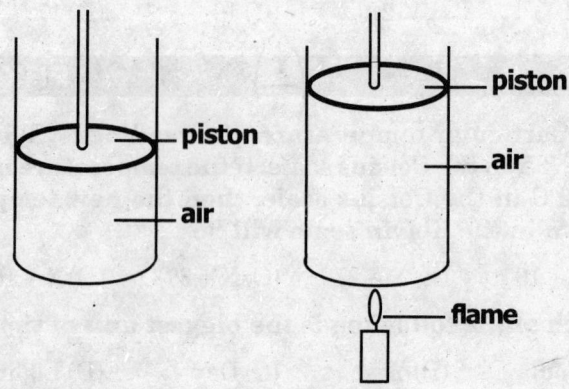

    Which of the following inferences can be drawn from the above experiment?

    (A) Heat cannot do any work.   (B) Work is done to compress a gas.

    (C) Heat can do work.   (D) Force cannot produce heat.

34. If the least count of an instrument is doubled, its accuracy:

    (A) is halved.   (B) is also doubled.

    (C) increases by four times.   (D) remains the same.

35. **The figures shown below represent the lever of the :**

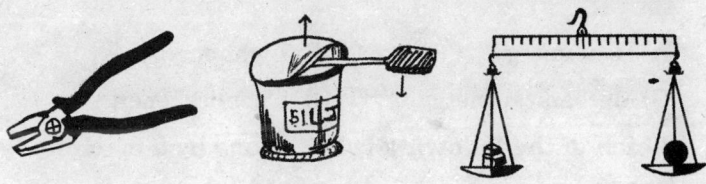

(A) 1st order (B) 2nd order

(C) 3rd order (D) 1st & 3rd order

36. **Study the Energy Venn - diagram given below :**

Sound
Light
Heat
Y
P
X
Z

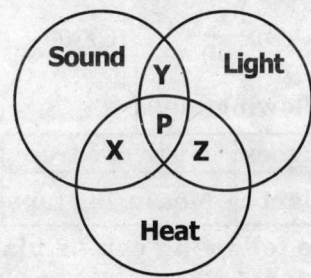

Which of the following can be placed in the area covered by Y ?

(A) Radio (B) Television (C) Heater (D) Bulb

37. **The handle of a motorbike is an example of which kind of simple machine ?**

(A) Inclined planes (B) Wedges

(C) Wheel-and-axle (D) Pulleys

38. **A ball thrown upwards from a running train follows a/an :**

(A) rectilinear motion (B) curvilinear motion

(C) rotational motion (D) oscillatory motion

39. **Study the following figures**

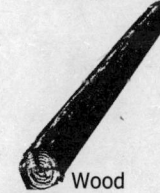

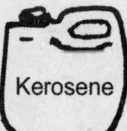

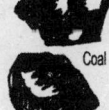

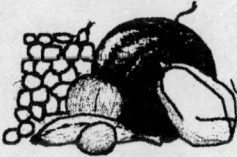

Wood
Kerosene
Coal
fruits

Which of the following energies is present in all of the above?

(A) Heat energy (B) Light energy
(C) Mechanical energy (D) Chemical energy

40. Which of the following is NOT done by a machine ?

    (A) Magnification of force. (B) Magnification of speed.
    (C) Magnification of load. (D) Changing the direction of force.

41. $1 \text{ g/cm}^3 = $ _____ kg/m^3

    (A) $\dfrac{1}{1000}$ (B) $\dfrac{1}{100}$ (C) 100 (D) 1000

42. Study the following table

Wt. of 10 mangoes	Girth of a tree	Volume of a stone
Weighing balance	Measuring tape	?

   Which of the following can be placed in the box that is blank ?

   (A) Stopwatch (B) Standard scale
   (C) Measuring jar (D) Thread & Scale

43. Which of the following statements is TRUE regarding a single pulley ?

    (A) Force is magnified in it. (B) Direction of force is changed.
    (C) Distance is magnified. (D) Both (A) and (B)

44. As we move from the equator to the poles, our weight :

    (A) decreases
    (B) increases
    (C) remains constant
    (D) varies with the atmospheric pressure

Model Paper - 1

45. When three immiscible liquids A, B and C were put in a jar the following was noticed :

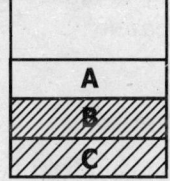

Which of the three liquids will exert the lowest pressure when taken separately ?

(A) A (B) B (C) C (D) Cannot be determined

46. When we touch a book and an iron rod both at the same temperature, we feel that the iron rod is colder. This is because :

(A) paper is a good conductor of heat.

(B) paper is a bad insulator of heat.

(C) iron is a good conductor of heat.

(D) iron is a bad conductor of heat.

47. When light falls on certain materials, they emit electrons. These electrons are called :

(A) photo-electrons (B) valency electrons

(C) bonded electrons (D) free electrons

48. A moving cricket ball hurts more than a moving tennis ball because :

(A) tennis ball is bigger (B) cricket ball has more density

(C) tennis ball has more mass (D) cricket ball is bigger

49. A second order lever :

(A) equals effort to the load (B) increases the effort required

(C) reduces the effort required (D) either B or C

50. The temperature recorded in Mussoorie on a certain day was 30 °C. Expressed in the kelvin scale, it will be :

(A) 203 K (B) 86 K (C) 313 K (D) 303 K

Model Paper - 1

CLASS: VI — CHEMISTRY

51. **Eventhough Mercury is closer to the Sun than Venus, it is colder. This is because :**
    (A) it is smaller
    (B) it does not have atmosphere
    (C) the period of rotation of Mercury is less than Venus
    (D) water vapour is present in Venus

52. **X & Y together form a solid-in-solid mixture. The sizes of X and Y vary considerably. Which of the following methods can be used to separate these ?**
    (A) Winnowing   (B) Sieving
    (C) Magnetic separation   (D) Sedimentation

53. **The fact that very hot lava comes out from volcanoes proves that the :**
    (A) interior of the earth is hot
    (B) exterior of the earth is hot
    (C) exterior of the earth is getting heated up
    (D) interior of the earth is getting heated up

54. **Study the following figures showing equal volumes of five different immiscible liquids P, Q, R, S & T in two containers :**

    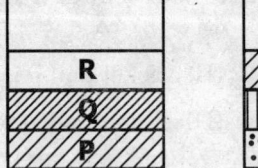 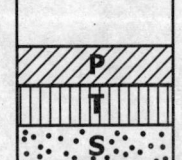

    Which of the following statements is TRUE ?
    (A) Liquid **P** is the heaviest of all.
    (B) Liquid **R** has the lowest density.
    (C) The density of **T** is less than the density of **Q**.
    (D) The density of **Q** is less than the density of **R**.

55. The shape of the Milky Way Galaxy is :
    (A) spherical (B) disc shaped
    (C) square planar (D) spiral
56. Ice is used to make igloos. This is because ice is a :
    (A) good conductor of heat (B) bad conductor of heat
    (C) fast conductor of heat (D) both B & C
57. Which of the following substances can be seen clearly because they reflect most of the light falling on them ?
    (A) Transparent (B) Translucent
    (C) Opaque (D) Both A & B
58. LPG cylinders used for cooking contain methane and butane gases. Together they form :
    (A) a homogeneous mixture (B) a heterogeneous mixture
    (C) an amalgam / alloy (D) a solid-in-gas mixture
59. The latest space mission of USA, 'Discovery' was primarily intended to :
    (A) explore the planet Uranus.
    (B) complete work on the International Space Station.
    (C) check for possible risks in the launching & landing of space shuttles.
    (D) launch a satellite.
60. When three substances X, Y & Z were heated, X changed directly into gas, Y started burning and Z melted. Which of the following statements is TRUE regarding the above experiment ?
    (A) X & Z undergo chemical changes that are fast.
    (B) Only Y undergoes a chemical change.
    (C) Y & Z undergo fast physical changes.
    (D) Only X undergoes a physical change.
61. The element that does not form compounds is :
    (A) nitrogen (B) neon (C) iron (D) oxygen

62. Which of the following is NOT made up of gases ?
   (A) Sun (B) Mercury
   (C) Tail of a comet (D) Proxima Centauri

63. Decantation is a method of separation used to separate liquids having different :
   (A) boiling points (B) densities
   (C) masses (D) colours

64. A substance 'X' has a fixed shape and volume. If heated, it loses its shape but not volume. What is 'X' ?
   (A) Solid (B) Liquid
   (C) Gas (D) None of these

65. Respiration of a relaxed person is a :
   (A) slow change (B) fast & periodic change
   (C) chemical change (D) both B & C

66. The ozone layer protects us from :
   (A) X-rays (B) ultraviolet rays
   (C) infrared rays (D) visible rays

67. The metal used as a catalyst in the hydrogenation of oils is :
   (A) Silicon (B) Nickel (C) Phosphorus (D) Hydrogen

68. Which of the following is a semiconductor ?
   (A) Copper (B) Silver (C) Silicon (D) Phosphorus

69. The most important characteristic of a pure liquid is its :
   (A) non-uniform composition (B) fixed colour
   (C) fixed weight (D) fixed boiling point

70. 'Law of conservation of mass', states that the total mass of the universe :
   (A) is always constant (B) increases gradually
   (C) decreases gradually (D) is never constant

CLASS: VI   Brain Mapping Academy

CLASS: VI   BIOLOGY

71. Which of the following does not form a group with the others ?

    (A) Bacteria   (B) Paramecium   (C) Fern   (D) Crystal

72. During which of the following processes is energy released ?

    (A) Excretion   (B) Digestion   (C) Respiration   (D) Circulation

73. Which of the following can grow without the formation of seeds ?

    (A) Peas   (B) Groundnut   (C) Mint   (D) Mustard

74. Which of the following is a Xerophyte ?

    (A) Lotus   (B) Aloe   (C) Hibiscus   (D) Algae

75. *Pisum sativum* is the scientific name of :

    (A) Rice   (B) Cat   (C) Pea   (D) Sunflower

76. Match the given figures correctly with the type of organisms given in the box and choose the correct answer.

(i)	(a) Bacteria
(ii)	(b) Fungi
(iii)	(c) Fern
(iv)	(d) Chlamydomonas (algae)

    (A) i-d, ii-c, iii-a, iv-b   (B) i-d, ii-b, iii-d, iv-a
    (C) i-c, ii-b, iii-d, iv-a   (D) i-a, ii-b, iii-c, iv-d

Model Paper - 1

77. Which of the following does not from a group with the others?

   (A) Aster (B) Mustard
   (C) Henna (D) Mint

78. Which of the following animals is NOT an invertebrate ?

   (A) Housefly (B) Octopus
   (C) Lady bird (D) Pomfret

79. Which of the following is used to flavour our food ?

   (A) Olive oil (B) Cocoa
   (C) Sugarcane (D) Garlic

80. Sago is obtained from :

   (A) mosses (B) ferns (C) cycads (D) algae

81. Which of the following is NOT matched correctly ?

   (A) Oysters - Pearl (B) Lac insect - Lac
   (C) Rats - Fur (D) Elephants - Ivory

82. The roots of a mangrove tree are also called :

   (A) supporting roots (B) breathing roots
   (C) prop roots (D) none of these

83. Which of the following parts of a plant is modified into a pitcher in Nepenthes ?

   (A) Stem (B) Leaf
   (C) Root (D) Flower

84. Skin is the part of ____ system

   (A) muscular (B) skeletal
   (C) circulatory (D) integumentary

85. Which of the following is NOT associated with the digestive system ?

   (A) Oesophagus (B) Rectum (C) Liver (D) Ureters

86. Which of the following is NOT matched correctly ?
    (A) Cerebrum - seat of intelligence
    (B) Endocrine glands - produce hormones
    (C) Ovaries - male reproductive organs
    (D) Skull - protects the brain
87. 'Adam's apple' in men is actually known as :
    (A) wind pipe   (B) Bronchi   (C) larynx   (D) trachea
88. Which of the following is used in crushing the food ?
    (A) incisors   (B) canines
    (C) premolars   (D) wisdom tooth
89. The total quantity of blood in a person is :
    (A) 3.5 l (B) 5.5 l
    (C) 7.5 l (D) 9.5 l
90. Which of the following is NOT a carnivorous plant ?

    i. 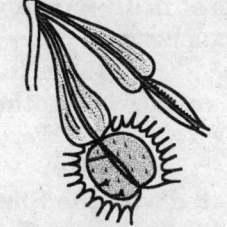   ii.

    iii. 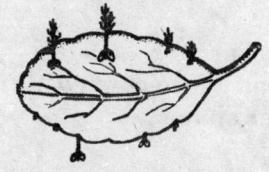   iv.

    (A) i only   (B) ii only
    (C) iii only   (D) Both iii and iv

Model Paper - 1

GENERAL QUESTIONS

91. Which of the following facts is NOT true regarding India?
    (A) It is the largest democracy
    (B) The oldest civilization was in it
    (C) It has the highest mountain
    (D) It has the largest number of post offices

92. Pointing to a photograph Sunny said "the father of this person is the grandfather of my son". If Sunny is the only son of his father, how is the person in the photograph related to Sunny ?
    (A) Aunt   (B) Uncle   (C) Nephew   (D) Sister

93. An object does not reflect light of any colour. It will be seen as :
    (A) White   (B) Colourless   (C) Black   (D) Green

94. The Vice President of India is :
    (A) B.S. Sekhawat   (B) Buta Singh
    (C) S.S. Barnala   (D) None of these

95. A person who knows many languages is called :
    (A) a polyglot   (B) a bilinguist
    (C) ambidextrous   (D) cosmopolitan

96. The film 'Bose - The Forgotten Hero', is directed by :
    (A) Aparna Sen   (B) Shyam Bengal
    (C) Satyajit Ray   (D) Mani Kaul

97. A number when divided by itself results in another one that is half of it. The number is :
    (A) 1   (B) 2   (C) 11   (D) 8197

98. Who among the following is associated with the 'Shehnai'?
    (A) Ustad Amjad Ali Khan   (B) Pandit Hari Prasad Chaurasia
    (C) Ustad Zakir Hussain   (D) Ustad Bismillah Khan

99. Which of the following does not form a group with the others ?
    (A) Cycle   (B) Scooter   (C) Car   (D) Bus

100. Which song did Rakesh Sharma use to convey his feelings when he saw India from outer space ?
    (A) Ab Tumhare Hawale Watan
    (B) Jana Gana Mana
    (C) Sare Jahan Se Achcha
    (D) Yeh Mera India

Model Paper - 1

CLASS: VI — Brain Mapping Academy

CLASS: VI **Model Paper - 2** **MATHEMATICS**

1. Sunil scored 1,086,000 points in a video game. Which of the following expressions below is equal to 1,086,000?

    (A) 100 + 80 + 6

    (B) 1,000 + 80 + 6

    (C) 1,000,000 + 80,000 + 6,000

    (D) 1,000,000 + 800,000 + 60,000

2. Which of the following best represents the location of point A on the number line shown below?

    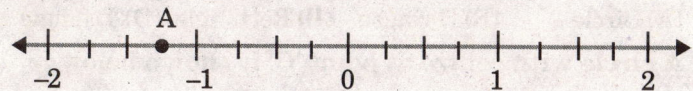

    (A) $-2\dfrac{3}{4}$ (B) $-2\dfrac{1}{4}$ (C) $-1\dfrac{1}{2}$ (D) $-1\dfrac{1}{4}$

3. Which picture below appears to have a single line of symmetry?

    (A) 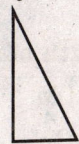   (B)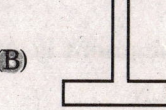

    (C) 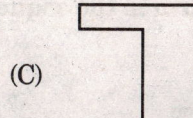   (D)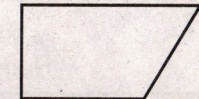

4. Which of the following number sentences is represented on the number line shown below?

    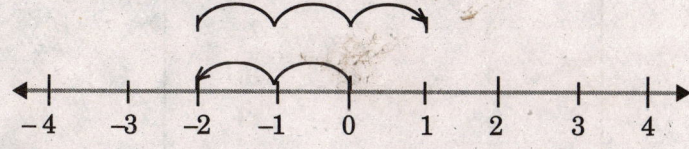

    (A) $-2 + 3 = 1$ (B) $1 - (+2) = -1$

    (C) $1 + (-2) = -2$ (D) $(-2) + (-3) = 1$

Model Paper - 2   17

5. For a craft project, Anil wanted to use wrapping paper to cover the outside of a coke container, a right circular cylinder. He did not want to cover the top or the bottom of the container.

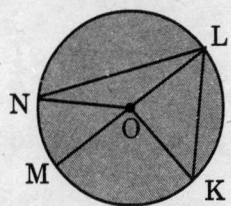

What two dimensional figure represents the shape of the piece of paper that would exactly cover the outside of the container ?

(A) Circle (B) Hexagon (C) Rectangle (D) Triangle

6. A circle with centre at point 'O' is shown below.

Which line segment is 2 times the length of radius OK ?

(A) Segment LN (B) Segment LM
(C) Segment LK (D) Segment ON

7. What is the rule to find the value of a term in the sequence below ?

Sequence

Position, n	Value of term
1	1
2	4
3	7
4	10
5	13
n	?

(A) n + 3 (B) 3n (C) n − 2 (D) 3n − 2

Model Paper - 2

8. The sum of any three angles of a rectangle is :

   (A) 360⁰   (B) 180⁰   (C) 270⁰   (D) 120⁰

9. What is the name of the only regular polygon which has as many diagonals as it has sides ?

   (A) Square   (B) Pentagon   (C) Hexagon   (D) Octagon

10. What is the product of two whole numbers whose difference is 1 ?

    (A) 63   (B) 80   (C) 90   (D) 99

11. If a rectangle with area 36 sq.m is not a square, its dimension cannot be :

    (A) 4 m   (B) 6 m   (C) 9 m   (D) 12 m

12. Four identical squares, lined up as shown, form a rectangle whose area is 144 sq units. What is the perimeter of the shaded region ?

    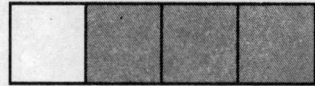

    (A) 36 units   (B) 48 units   (C) 60 units   (D) 108 units

13. You will get a triangle if you connect any three of the dots at the right. You can get at most _____ different such triangles.

    (A) 2   (B) 3   (C) 4   (D) 5

14. In the picture below, the area of triangle ABD is equal to 15 sq units, the area of triangle ABC is equal to 12 sq units and the area of triangle ABE is equal to 4 sq units. What is the area of pentagon ABCED ?

    (A) 23 sq units

    (B) 27 sq units

    (C) 31 sq units

    (D) 35 sq units

    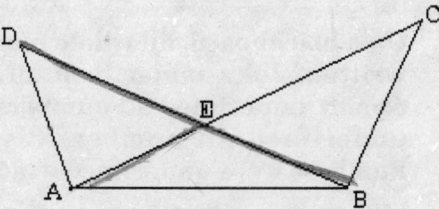

15. The least positive integer which is divisible by 2,3 and 4 is :

   (A) 36 (B) 24 (C) 18 (D) 12

16. A square with the length of side equal to 'x' consists of a square with an area of 81 cm^2, two rectangles with areas of 18 cm^2 each, and a small square. What is the value of 'x'?

   (A) 11 cm
   (B) 10 cm
   (C) 9 cm
   (D) 2 cm

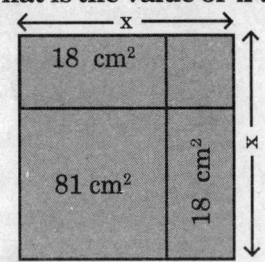

17. Which of the following numbers is NOT a factor of 2007 ?

   (A) 3 (B) 9 (C) 223 (D) 27

18. Ratio of 250 ml to 2 litres is :

   (A) 250 : 2 (B) 250 : 200 (C) 1 : 8 (D) 125 : 1

19. In $\frac{3}{4}p + 8 = 17$, the value of 'p' is :

   (A) –12 (B) 12 (C) 36 (D) –36

20. Which decimal number is greater than $\frac{1}{2}$?

   (A) 0.7 (B) 0.25 (C) 0.48 (D) 0.299

21. $100 - 4[25 - \{5 + (12 - 9)\}] = $ _____

   (A) –32 (B) 132 (C) 32 (D) –132

22. Number of line segments possible with three collinear points is :

   (A) 1 (B) 2 (C) 3 (D) infinite

23. On a blackboard, all whole numbers from 1 to 2007 were written. John underlined all numbers divisible by 2, Anand underlined all numbers divisible by 3 and Basha underlined all numbers divisible by 4. How many numbers were underlined exactly twice ?

   (A) 668 (B) 501 (C) 334 (D) 167

24. An elevator cannot carry more than 150 kg. Four friends weigh 60 kg, 80 kg, 80 kg and 80 kg respectively. What is the least number of trips necessary to carry the four friends to the highest floor ?

    (A) 1 (B) 2 (C) 3 (D) 4

25. In a two – digit number, 'a' is the tens digit and 'b' is the ones digit. Which of the conditions below ensures that the number will be divisible by 6 ?

    (A) a + b = 6 (B) b = 6a (C) b = 5a (D) b = 2a

CLASS: VI — PHYSICS

26. Harish has set up a circuit as shown. Which of the following should he put in the blank box to make the bulb glow more brightly ?

    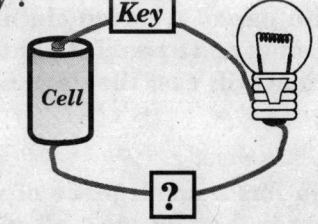

    (A) Bulb
    (B) Cell
    (C) Key
    (D) Wire

27. Manisha is taller than Neha by 3 cm. If the height of Manisha is 1.1 m, what will be the height of Neha?

    (A) 1.4 m (B) 0.8 m
    (C) 1.07 m (D) 10.4 m

28. A compass can be used to :

    Compass

    (A) find the gravitational force of a place
    (B) find the centre of gravity of a body
    (C) find the altitude of a place
    (D) find all the directions of a place

29. Which of the following is NOT in periodic motion?

    (A) A fan moving at constant speed
    (B) A swinging pendulum
    (C) Motion of earth
    (D) A flying kite

Model Paper - 2

30. Which of the following shows the energy changes that take place when a bulb glows?

(A) Chemical energy → Electrical energy → Heat energy → Light energy

(B) Electrical energy → Chemical energy → Light energy → Heat energy

(C) Heat energy → Light energy → Electrical energy

(D) Light energy → Heat energy → Chemical energy

31. A thin paper, a cotton cloth, a glass sheet and a mirror are taken and a beam of light is directed onto them. Which of them will cast the darkest shadow?

(A) Paper   (B) Cotton cloth
(C) Glass sheet   (D) Mirror

32. Pooja has a small piece of metal and a thread. To find whether the piece is a magnet or not, she :

(A) requires a piece of magnetic substance

(B) requires a piece of non-magnetic substance

(C) requires a magnet or a compass

(D) does not require anything else

33. The graph shown here shows the motion of four runners - Rajesh, Winston, Prakash and Rahul in a 5 km marathon. Whose motion is the fastest?

(A) Rajesh
(B) Winston
(C) Prakash
(D) Rahul

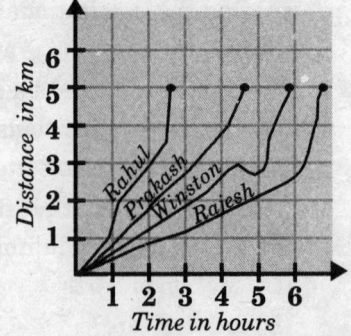

Model Paper - 2

34. Which of the following is NOT correct regarding light?
    (A) Light is a form of energy.
    (B) Light can not be changed into other forms of energy.
    (C) Light always travels in a straight line.
    (D) Light can be reflected from an object.

35. In the boxes shown here, articles from which box(es) can be attracted by magnets but cannot attract other objects? 
    (A) P
    (B) Q
    (C) R
    (D) Both P & Q

P	Q	R
Magnetic Substances	Magnets	Non-magnetic substances

36. Bulb in which of the following arrangements will be able to glow?

    (A)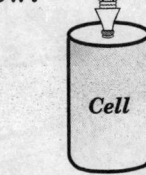
    (B)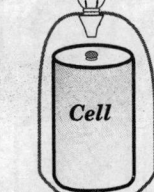
    (C)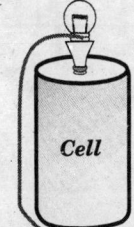
    (D)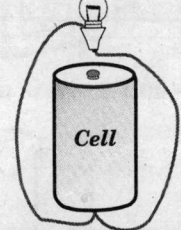

37. Which of the given sets of magnets will repel each other?

    (A)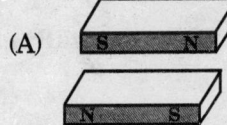
    (B)
    (C)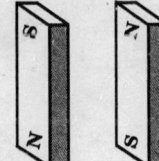
    (D)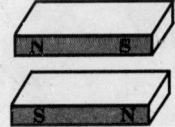

Model Paper - 3   23

38. A car moving in a straight road first increases its speed and then comes to stop suddenly. During this time the tyres of the car have undergone :

(A) only rectilinear motion

(B) only circular motion

(C) rectilinear, circular and periodic motion

(D) rectilinear, circular but not periodic motion

39. Which of the following shows the correct mirror image of the letter 'P' ?

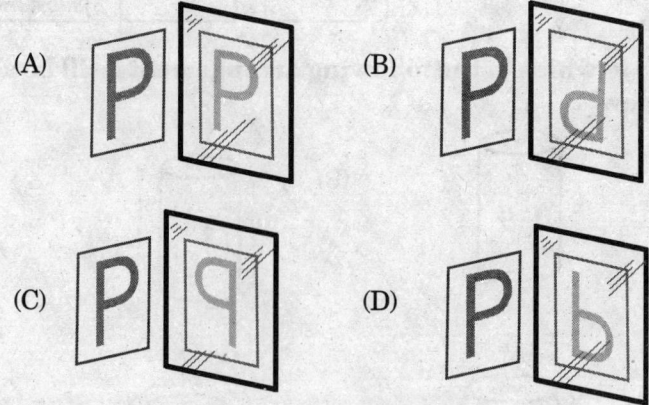

40. The given figure is a 'material tester'.

Which of the following objects will make the bulb glow when put in the gap shown ?

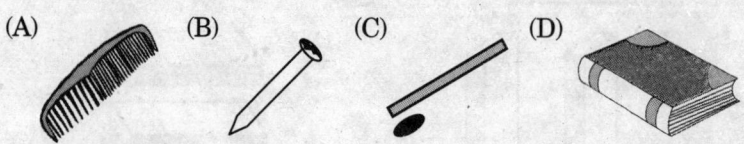

41. The girl in the given figure is able to see the dog because:

   (A) light is falling on the dog
   (B) it is dark
   (C) light gets reflected from the dog to the girl's eyes
   (D) light from the bulb is reaching the girl's eyes

42. Which of the following could be the speed of a man walking leisurely around a park ?
   (A) 50 metres per second   (B) 4 kilometer per hour
   (C) 1000 cm per second   (D) 1.5 kilometer per minute

43. In which circuit will the bulb or bulbs glow the brightest?
   (A) A simple circuit with one bulb and one cell
   (B) A simple circuit with one bulb and two cells
   (C) A simple circuit with two bulbs and one cell
   (D) A simple circuit with two bulbs and two cells

44. An electric heater is used to convert electrical energy to:
   (A) heat energy   (B) light energy
   (C) both A & B   (D) chemical energy

45. Which of the following structures can cast a shadow like ?

   (A)  (B)  (C) 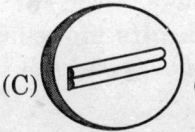 (D)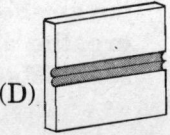

46. The figure shows how a compass behaves when a magnet is brought near it.

   How will the compass be when the magnet is turned by 180° ?

   (A)  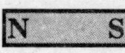   (B)

Model Paper - 2

(C) 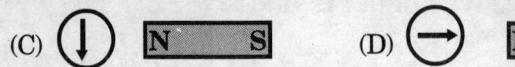 (D)

47. When the two terminals of a cell are connected directly with a wire, then :
    (A) more electrical energy is stored in the cell
    (B) the chemicals get used up very fast
    (C) no current flows
    (D) the cell explodes

48. Which of the following can be attracted by a magnet?
    (A) Magnetic substances   (B) Non-magnetic substances
    (C) Magnets   (D) Both A and C

49. Wires conducting electricity are usually covered with plastic or rubber. This is done mainly to :
    (A) avoid cuts and injury   (B) prevent rusting
    (C) prevent shocks   (D) make them beautiful

50. For the magnet shown here, at which place will the force of magnetism be the maximum ?
    (A) 1   (B) 2
    (C) 3   (D) 4

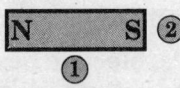

CLASS: VI — CHEMISTRY

51. In an experiment, scientists put a mouse in an airtight jar as shown. After some time the mouse struggled to breathe and its movements reduced. What should the scientists do to make it live longer ?

    (A) Put another mouse in it
    (B) Put a plant in it
    (C) Keep some water inside the jar
    (D) Keep a burning candle inside the jar

52. Compared to plain water, more dirt is removed from the clothes when some detergent is added to it. We can say that detergents :

    (A) increase the solubility of water
    (B) increase the weight of the dirt particles
    (C) decrease the density of water
    (D) increase the temperature of water

53. Which of the following is NOT a chemical change?

    (A) A banana turning brown.
    (B) Moulding a piece of gold into a ring.
    (C) Curdling of milk.
    (D) Baking of a cake.

54. Balloons, tyre tubes and football-bladders are made of rubber. This is because rubber is :

    (A) inexpensive   (B) a natural product
    (C) an electrical insulator   (D) soft and flexible

55. To separate the constituents of a mixture a student carried out the actions shown in the flow chart given here. What could 'Y' and 'Z' be respectively?

    (A) Stones and rice
    (B) Sand and sugar
    (C) Sand and glass
    (D) Hydrogen and salt

    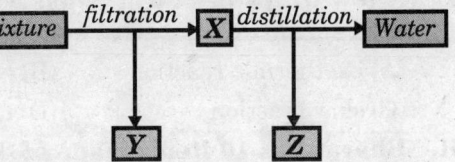

56. Pooja took two same sized balloons X and Y and blew the X balloon. She then connected them with a hollow pipe as shown here. What will Pooja find ?

    (A) X becomes bigger and Y smaller.
    (B) Y becomes bigger than X.
    (C) Both become big till they burst.
    (D) Both attain the same size.

    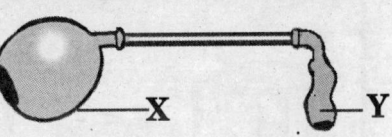

57. **Why is it desirable to water plants early in the morning?**
    (A) Plants absorb water only in the morning.
    (B) Less water evaporates in the morning.
    (C) Water used in the morning can be reused later.
    (D) There is more water available in the morning.

58. **We can observe tiny droplets on the outside of cold soft drink bottles. This shows that :**

    (A) glass melts on heating
    (B) air contains water vapour
    (C) glass cracks on being cooled
    (D) water evaporates on cooling

59. **A few coloured glass pieces that are big in size are mixed with sugar. What is the easiest way to separate them ?**
    (A) Heat the mixture
    (B) Add the mixture to water and filter
    (C) Handpick the glass pieces
    (D) Handpick the sugar particles

60. **A few drops of petrol when put in our hand gives us a cold sensation as petrol evaporates. This change is a/an :**
    (A) exothermic reaction   (B) endothermic reaction
    (C) slow reaction   (D) fast combination reaction

61. **Bharat has 10 items made of different materials and of different shapes and sizes. He wants to group the materials from which they are made into two groups-heavy and light. What would be a good way to do this ?**

(A) Find whether they sink or float in water
(B) Find out the mass of each item
(C) Find the volume of each item
(D) Find whether they are soluble in water

62. **Rusting of iron is a chemical change because :**
    (A) it is a temporary change
    (B) it is a slow reaction
    (C) a new substance is formed
    (D) upon cleaning the original substance is recovered

63. **The humidity of a place :**
    (A) lies between 10 – 20 %   (B) is always more than 60 %
    (C) is always less than 60 %   (D) varies from time to time

64. **Which of the following helps us sip a soft drink with a straw?**
    (A) The difference in the atmospheric pressure and our mouth.
    (B) The difference in the temperature of the drink and our mouth.
    (C) The density and height of the drink.
    (D) Gravity of the place.

65. **A drop of water falling on a hot glowing bulb causes it to burst. This is because :**
    (A) glass reacts with water explosively.
    (B) the reaction between glass and water is exothermic.
    (C) glass is a good conductor of electricity.
    (D) glass is a bad conductor of heat.

66. **A vendor sells white powdered salt mixed with white powdered stone. The knowledge of which property will help you to detect this practice ?**
    (A) Density   (B) Solubility
    (C) Opacity   (D) Appearance

67. It is difficult to use matchsticks made of wax when compared to the ones made of wood, because of smaller length. Why can not be the wax matchsticks made longer ?
   (A) Longer wax matchsticks would not burn
   (B) Longer wax matchsticks are expensive
   (C) Longer wax matchsticks break easily
   (D) Shorter wax matchsticks save space
68. The main source of water for inland lakes and wells is/are:
   (A) snow (B) ground water (C) sea water (D) plants
69. Rain water harvesting is a method employed to :
   (A) stop soil erosion in a place
   (B) control floods in a place
   (C) raise the water table of a place
   (D) cause rains by cloud seeding
70. Carbon powder and iron filings are both black powders. Which of the following will help you to separate iron filings from carbon powder ?
   (A) Magnifying lens   (B) Magnet
   (C) Heat   (D) Water

CLASS: VI — BIOLOGY

71. Which of the following are called 'body building' foods ?
   (A) Carbohydrates   (B) Proteins
   (C) Vitamins   (D) Fats
72. Given below are the symptoms of a disease.
   i. Weak muscles
   ii. Very little energy to do work
   These are the symptoms of :
   (A) Scurvy   (B) Rickets
   (C) Beriberi   (D) Anaemia

73. Observe the figure given here. Which of the following is the correct reason for the bending of the plant ?

   (A) The plant is not having enough place to grow upright
   (B) The plant bends due to external pressure
   (C) The plant is responding to light
   (D) The plant bends because of the weight of the leaves

74. Which of the following is the correct sequence followed in making a cotton fabric ?
   (A) Weaving → spinning → picking → ginning
   (B) Picking → ginning → spinning → weaving
   (C) Picking → spinning → ginning → weaving
   (D) Spinning → ginning → weaving → picking

75. Which of the following is used to see the shape of bones?
   (A) ECG   (B) Ultrasound   (C) X-ray   (D) Photograph

76. Which of the following worms are used in vermi-composting ?
   (A) Roundworms   (B) Ringworms
   (C) Redworms   (D) Flatworms

77. Match the following and select the correct answer.

a. Ball and socket joint	1. Knee
b. Hinge joint	2. Neck and head
c. Pivotal joint	3. Jaws
d. Fixed point	4. Shoulder

   (A) a - 4, b - 2, c - 3, d - 1   (B) a - 4, b - 1, c - 2, d - 3
   (C) a - 4, b - 3, c - 1, d - 2   (D) a - 4, b - 1, c - 3, d - 2

78. The cross section of a flower is shown here. Fertilisation takes place in which of the following labelled parts?

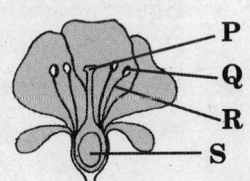

   (A) P   (B) Q   (C) R   (D) S

Model Paper - 2

79. Which of the following characteristics helps a bird in flying?
    (A) Weak but heavy skeleton
    (B) Hollow and light limb bones
    (C) Their body temperature depends on surrounding
    (D) Heavy bones that have bone marrow
80. Given below are some animals and their locomotory organs. Find the pair that is NOT matched correctly?
    (A) Snakes - scales   (B) Earthworm - body segments
    (C) Man - forelimbs   (D) Fish - fins
81. The deficiency of which of the following causes anaemia?
    (A) Calcium   (B) Iodine   (C) Magnesium   (D) Iron
82. Fibre is obtained from which part of the cotton plant?
    (A) Stem   (B) Leaf   (C) Seed   (D) Fruit
83. Which of the following is NOT the function of the stem :
    (A) It gives support to the plant
    (B) It conducts water, minerals and food to the plant
    (C) It fixes the plant in the soil
    (D) It bears fruits, flowers and leaves
84. Which of the following is NOT paired correctly?
    (A) Desert plant - Cactus   (B) Aquatic plant - Pistia
    (C) Cold region - Snow leopard (D) Desert animal Tiger
85. Which of the following is an artificial fibre?
    (A) Nylon   (B) Jute   (C) Wool   (D) Silk
86. Which part of the leaf signifies the root system present in that plant?
    (A) Leaf petiole   (B) Leaf lamina
    (C) Leaf venation   (D) Leaf colour
87. Which of the following body parts is most likely to help a tiger camouflaging itself for catching the prey?
    (A) Body shape (B) Eyes   (C) Stripes   (D) Nails
88. Which of the following is a desert plant?
    (A) Hibiscus   (B) Pistia   (C) Aloevera   (D) Eucalyptus

Model Paper - 2

89. Study the relationship given in Set-I and find the missing part in Set-II.

Set-I	
Papaya Carrot Eggs	Vit - A

Set-II	
Tamato Orange Lemon Guava	?

   (A) Vit - D   (B) Vit - C   (C) Vit - E   (D) Vit - B

90. Which of the following methods is used to separate heavier and lighter components of a mixture by blowing air ?
   (A) Threshing   (B) Seiving
   (C) Winnowing   (D) Sedimentation

CLASS: VI — GENERAL QUESTIONS

91. What is the missing character inbetween the letters given below, so that two words are formed?

   SLO ? IDE

   (A) S   (B) W   (C) A   (D) R

92. Which number should come next in the series given here?

   16, 14, 12, 10, ?

   (A) 11   (B) 9   (C) 8   (D) 7

93. The founder of Grameena Bank, who won the Nobel Prize, is from :
   (A) India   (B) Bangladesh   (C) China   (D) Turkey

94. An aeroplane is to air, as a submarine is to :
   (A) air   (B) land   (C) water   (D) forest

95. Meteorology is the science of :
   (A) metals   (B) volcanoes
   (C) meteors   (D) weather

Model Paper - 2

96. When was the atom bomb dropped in Hiroshima, Japan?
    (A) 1912   (B) 1945
    (C) 1975   (D) 1999

97. Who was the Prime Minister of India before Manmohan Singh?
    (A) P.V.Narasimha Rao   (B) L.K.Advani
    (C) Atal Behari Vajpayee   (D) I.K.Gujral

98. Which figure will come next in the series given below?

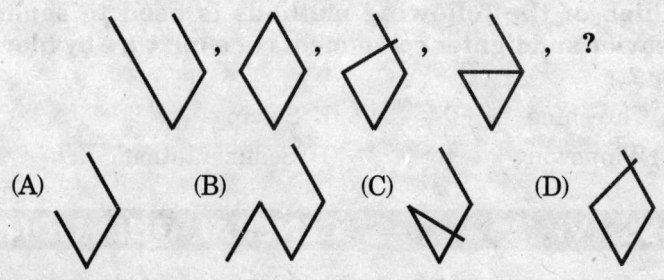

    (A)   (B)   (C)   (D)

99. In computers the command 'Control-P', helps you to :
    (A) save documents   (B) print documents
    (C) delete documents   (D) shut down

100. Hrishikesh Mukherjee, Akira Kurosawa and Steven Speilberg are all:
    (A) musicians   (B) writers
    (C) scientists   (D) film makers

CLASS: VI   Model Paper - 3   MATHEMATICS

1. Which of the following is true?
   (A) 130 ÷ 0 = 0
   (B) 150 ÷ 1 = 50
   (C) 0 × 130 = 0
   (D) 150 × 1 = 151

2. The diagram below is a number line.

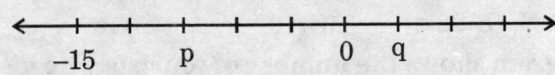

   ←—+—+—+—+—+—+—+—+—→
     −15   p   0   q

   What is the value of p + q?
   (A) −9   (B) −6   (C) −3   (D) 3

3. A class has 40 students. Every student contributed ₹ 2.50 to the class fund. $\frac{3}{10}$ of the total fund was used by the class to buy prizes for a Mathematics quiz. How much money does the class fund have left?
   (A) ₹ 30   (B) ₹ 50   (C) ₹ 70   (D) ₹ 90

4. Asha had 50 m of cloth. She used 27.8 m of the cloth and sold the rest to Krishna at ₹ 1.70 a metre. How much did Krishna pay Asha?
   (A) ₹ 30.74   (B) ₹ 35.74   (C) ₹ 36.74   (D) ₹ 37.74

5. In the diagram, the area of the rectangle ABCD is 50 cm^2.

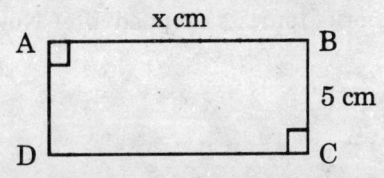

   ```
            x cm
        A┌────────┐B
         │        │
         │        │ 5 cm
         │        │
        D└────────┘C
   ```

   Find the value of x in the diagram.
   (A) 5   (B) 10   (C) 15   (D) 20

6. −4(−3+y)+7y = _____
   (A) 3y + 12   (B) 3y − 12   (C) y + 12   (D) y − 12

7. The diagram shows the selling price of pens in a shop. Anurag paid ₹ 50 for the purchase of a few pens and received ₹ 0.50 in change.

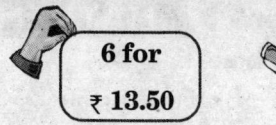

How many pens did Anurag buy?

(A) 26   (B) 22   (C) 19   (D) 16

8. The pictogram shows the number of tourists who visited a museum.

October   🧍🧍🧍🧍

November   🧍🧍🧍🧍🧍🧍

December   🧍🧍🧍🧍🧍🧍🧍🧍🧍

🧍 represents 100 tourists

Which of the following statement is true?

(A) The number of tourists in November and December are the same.
(B) The month of October has the most number of tourists.
(C) The difference in the number of tourists between November and December is 300.
(D) The number of tourists dropped after November.

9.

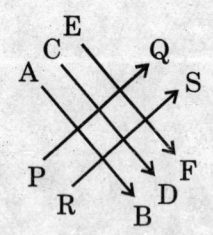

Which of the above lines is parallel to line PQ?

(A) AB   (B) CD   (C) EF   (D) RS

10. Indian cricket team won $\frac{4}{5}$ of its games. What is another way to write this number?

(A) 0.2   (B) 0.4   (C) 0.5   (D) 0.8

Model Paper - 3

11. Two plant pots are geometrically similar. The height of the smaller pot is 5 cm. The height of the larger pot is 15 cm.

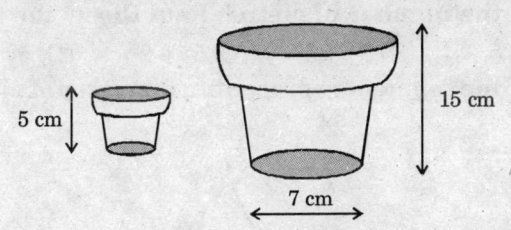

The diameter of the base of the larger pot is 7 cm. The diameter of the base of the smaller pot is:

(A) $2\frac{1}{3}$ cm (B) 3 cm (C) 7 cm (D) None of these

12. The diagram shows a fuel gauge in a car.

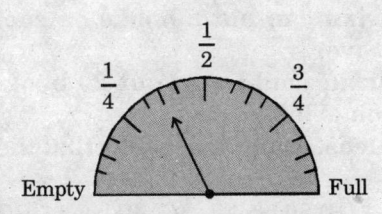

What fraction does the gauge show?

(A) $\frac{1}{8}$ (B) $\frac{3}{8}$ (C) $\frac{5}{4}$ (D) $\frac{1}{6}$

13. There are 30 pencils left at a school store after Shilpa buys a certain number of pencils, p. Devi buys 4 times as many pencils as Shilpa. The expression below shows the number of pencils remaining at the store after Devi buys her pencils.

$$30 - 4 \times p$$

How many pencils remain at the store if Shilpa bought 3 pencils?

(A) 14 (B) 18 (C) 78 (D) 104

14. Which equation shows the zero property of multiplication?

(A) $9 \times 0 = 0$ (B) $9 \times 0 = 9$ (C) $9 \times 0 = 1$ (D) $9 \times 1 = 0$

Model Paper - 3

15. Paul threw a football 5 more than twice the number of metres, y, that John threw. Which expression can be used to find the number of metres Paul threw the football?
    (A) 2y – 5   (B) 2y + 5   (C) 5y – 2   (D) 5y + 2
16. Which line segment represents a diameter of circle shown below?

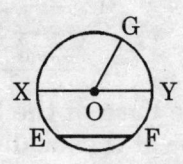

    (A) $\overline{XY}$ (B) $\overline{OY}$ (C) $\overline{OG}$ (D) $\overline{EF}$
17. A librarian is placing books on shelves.
    ❖ The librarian has more than 20 books.
    ❖ The librarian can put 8 books on each shelf with no books left over.
    ❖ The librarian could also put 20 books on each shelf with no books left over.
    Which is the least number of books that the librarian could have?
    (A) 160 books   (B) 80 books   (C) 40 books   (D) 28 books
18. Which expression completes the equation
    (19 × 3) + (19 × 1) = ☐ ?
    (A) (19 + 3) × (19 + 1)   (B) (19 + 19) × (3+ 1)
    (C) 19 + (3 × 1)   (D) 19 × (3 + 1)
19. The table below shows the time it takes Sudha to run different distances.

Time (in seconds)	Distance of Run (in metres)
10	6
20	12
30	18
40	24

    Based on the pattern shown in the table, how many metres can Sudha run in 70 seconds?
    (A) 24 metres   (B) 35 metres   (C) 42 metres   (D) 48 metres

20. Bunny is 12 years old. He writes an equation to find his mother's age, m.

    m – 12 = 35

    which operation solves the equation for m?

    (A) add 12 to both sides (B) subtract 12 from both sides
    (C) multiply both sides by 12 (D) divide both sides by 12

21. Which rectangle has an area of 24 square units and a perimeter of 20 units?

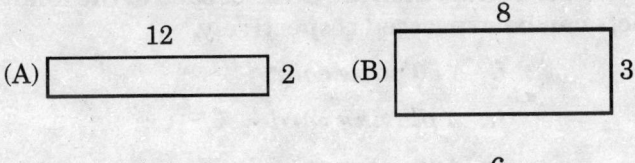

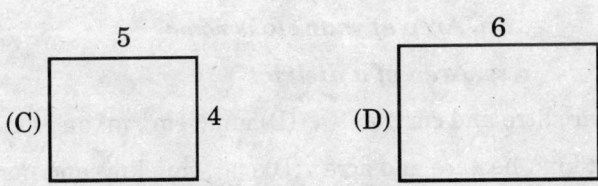

    (A) 12 × 2
    (B) 8 × 3
    (C) 5 × 4
    (D) 6 × 4

22. The least whole number is:

    (A) 0 (B) 1 (C) 10 (D) 101

23. The prime number which comes just after 19 is:

    (A) 20 (B) 21 (C) 22 (D) 23

24. The greatest negative integer is:

    (A) 0 (B) –5 (C) –1 (D) –1000

25. The place value of 5 in 1.532 is:

    (A) 5 (B) 50 (C) $\dfrac{5}{10}$ (D) $\dfrac{5}{1000}$

PHYSICS

26. **Lunar eclipse occurs when:**

    (A) the Sun is between the Earth and the Moon

    (B) the Moon is between the Sun and the Earth

    (C) the Earth is between the Sun and the Moon

    (D) it is a new moon day

27. **Name the units in which the areas of each of the following objects can be expressed respectively.**

    i. A 50 paise coin

    ii. A playing card

    iii. Area of your class room

    iv. Area of a district

    (A) kg^2, m^2, litre and cm^2 (B) mm^2, cm^2, m^2 and km^2

    (C) mm^2, km^2, hectare and acre   (D) cm^2, cm^2, km^2 and mm^2

28. **Shadows are:**

    (A) virtual   (B) real   (C) illusions   (D) permanent

29. **A camera flash is used in front of a mirror to take a photograph of the image of an object in the mirror. Then:**

    (A) the photograph of the image will be clearer

    (B) the photograph of the image will be brighter

    (C) the photograph of the object will be more beautiful

    (D) the photograph will not show anything except white colour

30. **Select the correct statement.**

    (A) In linear motion all bodies have a definite position of rest

    (B) In oscillatory motion all bodies have a definite position of rest

    (C) Swinging of a ball is an example of circular motion

    (D) Earth undergoes translatory motion during its rotation on its own axis.

31. Which of the following can be used to find the volume of a liquid?

   (A) A measuring jar (B) A metre scale
   (C) A beam balance (D) A barometer

32. On a track of 120 km, a train covers the first 30 km at a uniform speed of 45 km per hour. How fast must the train travel the next 90 km, so as to get an average speed of 60 km per hour for the entire trip?

   (A) 66.7 km/h (B) 62.5 km/h (C) 68.6 km/h (D) 67.5 km/h

33. A periscope in a submarine helps in viewing those objects:

   (A) that are very far.
   (B) that do not emit any light.
   (C) that are below the surface of water.
   (D) that are above the surface of water.

34. In which of the following, shapes can artificial magnets be prepared from magnetic materials?

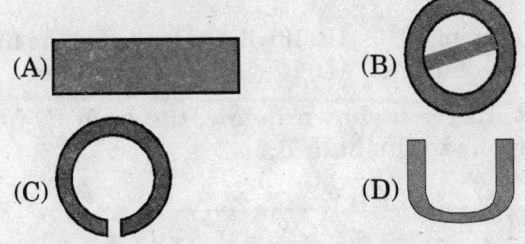

   (A)   (B)
   (C)   (D)

35. If a tunnel is dug along the diameter of the earth and a ball is dropped into the tunnel, it will execute:

   (A) linear motion (B) circular motion
   (C) oscillatory motion (D) translatory motion

36. Which of these represents one complete oscillation of the pendulum shown below?

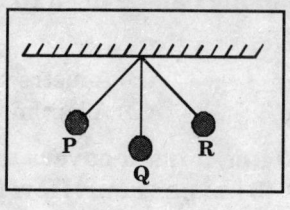

(A) PQR (B) PQQP (C) QRRP (D) PQR RQP

37. **A freely suspended magnet shows the North–South direction of a place. This is because:**

    (A) the geographic north is the magnetic north of the earth.
    (B) the geographic south is the magnetic south of the earth.
    (C) the geographic north is the magnetic south of the earth.
    (D) the geographic poles of the earth are the same as its magnetic poles.

38. **Pooja connects a second cell in a simple circuit in series with the first. How will this affect the brightness of the bulb in the circuit?**

    (A) It will stop glowing. (B) It will cause the bulb to fuse.
    (C) It will become dimmer. (D) It will become brighter.

39. **In the circuit diagram shown below, the bulb B_1 fuses off. What happens to the bulb B_2?**

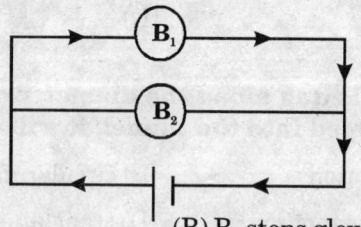

    (A) B_2 fuses off (B) B_2 stops glowing
    (C) B_2 glows as usual (D) B_2 glows dimmer than before

40. **Which of the following is false?**

    (A) Magnetic dipoles exist.
    (B) Magnetic unipoles exist.
    (C) Magnets always have N and S poles.
    (D) Like poles repel each other.

Model Paper - 3

41. Which of the following is used to pump water from a well to the overhead tank ?

(A) Generator (B) Motor (C) Dynamo (D) Transformer

42. In which of the following will there be a flow of current?

(A)   (B)

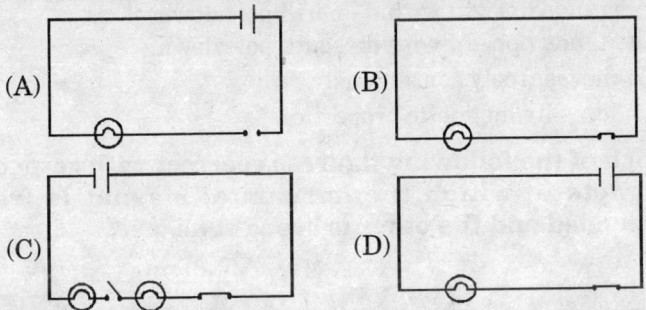

(C)   (D)

43. Which of the following non metals is a good conductor of electricity?

(A) Hydrogen gas   (B) Diamond
(C) Sulphur   (D) Graphite

44. Which of the following does not make use of a magnet?

(A) An electric torch   (B) A radio set
(C) An electric fan   (D) Both B and C

45. A satellite is orbiting the earth in such a manner that the satellite is always straight above India. It is at a height of 4,000 km. Which of the following is true?

(A) Its period of rotation is 24 hours.
(B) Its period of revolution is 24 hours
(C) Its period of rotation is 48 hours.
(D) Its period of revolution is 48 hours.

46. Match the following and select the correct answer.

Instruments	Energy conversions
1. Loud speaker	A. Electrical energy ⟶ Heat energy
2. Iron box	B. Electrical energy ⟶ Heat energy + Light energy
3. Television	C. Electrical energy ⟶ Sound energy
4. Electric bulb	D. Electrical energy ⟶ Light energy + Sound energy

Model Paper - 3

(A) 1 - C, 2 - A, 3 - B, 4 - D (B) 1 - A, 2 - C, 3 - D, 4 - B
(C) 1 - C, 2 - D, 3 - A, 4 - B (D) 1 - C, 2 - A, 3 - D, 4 - B

47. When a freely suspended magnetic needle is taken to the magnetic north pole of the earth:

(A) it stands upright with its north pole down.
(B) it stands upright with its south pole down.
(C) it moves freely continuously.
(D) it loses its magnetic properties.

48. Which of the following figures is correct with respect to magnets in which the horizontal magnet is freely suspended and the other is brought near it?

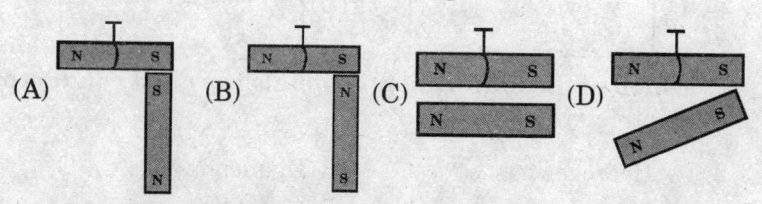

49. Nidhi has two bulbs connected across two cells in a simple circuit. How can she make the bulbs glow dimmer?

(A) Replace one cell with a piece of chalk
(B) Replace one cell with a piece of wire
(C) Replace one bulb with a piece of wire
(D) Replace one bulb with another cell

50. A bar magnet is cut into two without any loss of magnetic property as shown. Which of the following will be true?

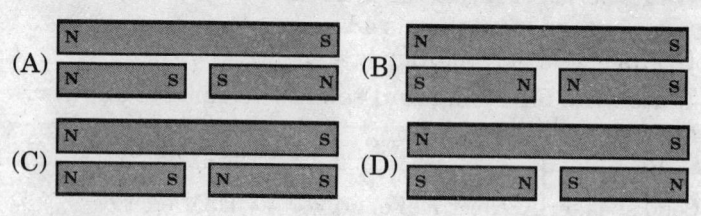

Model Paper - 3

CLASS: VI — CHEMISTRY

51. Melting of ice is an example of:

(A) an exothermic reaction (B) an endothermic reaction
(C) a chemical combination (D) a chemical decomposition

52. Study the changes given below for substances P and Q.

P	Q
fixed shape	no fixed shape
fixed volume	no fixed volume

What could be the substances P and Q?

(A) P–Paraffin wax, Q–Water vapour

(B) P–Ice, Q–Petrol

(C) P–Ethyl alcohol, Q–Sulphuric acid

(D) P–Paraffin wax, Q–Iodine vapours

53. Which of the following is the easiest to change ?

(A) The colour of your hair.

(B) The shape of your face.

(C) The colour of your eyes.

(D) Both A & C

54. Which of these is a chemical combination reaction?

(A) Drying of clothes in the wind.

(B) Freezing of water.

(C) Burning of hydrogen to give water.

(D) Melting of ice on heating.

55. Which of the following is NOT a homogeneous mixture?

(A) Sugar + water   (B) Sulphuric acid + water
(C) Kerosene + Petrol   (D) Petrol + water

56. The magnetic properties of iron disappear when it is heated strongly. This is:

   (A) a chemical change
   (B) an irreversible reaction
   (C) a physical change
   (D) a periodic change

57. A liquid that is two times heavier than water is mixed with another liquid that is lighter than water. What is the easiest way to separate these two immiscible liquids?

   (A) Filtration   (B) Separating funnel
   (C) Evaporation   (D) Distillation

58. The easiest way to separate a mixture of saw dust, iron filings and salt is:

   (A) magnetic separation–evaporation–add water–filtration
   (B) magnetic separation–add water–filtration–evaporation
   (C) evaporation–filtration–evaporation–magnetic separation
   (D) add water–filtration–evaporation–magnetic seperation

59. Threshing is a method of separation used to separate:

   (A) two useful substances of the same size
   (B) harmful substances from the useful ones
   (C) the useful substance from the non-useful ones
   (D) substances of different colours

60. Which of the following is an exothermic reaction?

   (A) Adding quick lime to water   (B) Adding ice to water
   (C) Melting of wax   (D) Melting of iron

61. Smoke in a closed room makes the walls black. This is because smoke is a:

   (A) gas-in-solid mixture   (B) solid-in-liquid mixture
   (C) gas-in-gas mixture   (D) solid-in-gas mixture

Model Paper - 3

62. Some water was left in a saucer in a room as shown below.

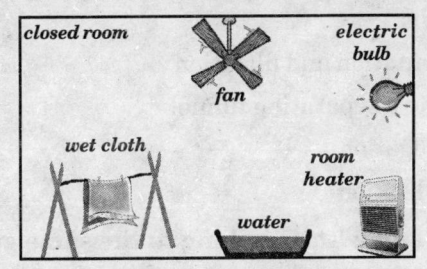

[closed room with fan, electric bulb, wet cloth, room heater, water]

Which of these must you remove from the room to make the water evaporate faster?

(A) Fan (B) Electric bulb
(C) Wet cloth (D) Room heater

63. Sieving can be used only when the components of the mixture have:

(A) different sizes

(B) different melting points

(C) different boiling points

(D) different specific gravities

64. Alum is added to the water in wells to:

(A) aid sedimentation

(B) aid filtration

(C) kill harmful organisms

(D) improve the nutritional value of water

65. We sprinkle water in a dirty room before sweeping because:

(A) water makes sweeping easier

(B) water repels the dust particles

(C) water coagulates the dust particles

(D) water dissolves the dust particles

66. The easiest way to separate a heterogeneous liquid mixture is:
    (A) sedimentation and filtration
    (B) by using a separating funnel
    (C) centrifugation
    (D) crystallisation

67. A needle and a knife belong to the same group because:
    (A) they are transparent
    (B) they are hard and magnetic
    (C) they float on water
    (D) they are poor conductors of heat

68. The purest form of natural water is obtained by the process of:
    (A) evaporation   (B) sublimation
    (C) precipitation   (D) seepage

69. A vendor sells white powdered salt mixed with white powdered stone. The knowledge of which property will help you detect this malpractice?
    (A) Ductility   (B) Opacity
    (C) Density   (D) Solubility

70. The solubility of oxygen in water:
    (A) increases with increase in temperature
    (B) decreases with increase in temperature
    (C) does not depend on temperature
    (D) is the highest at 100 °C

71. Which of the following processes liberate carbon dioxide in the air?

   X – Photosynthesis
   Y – Respiration
   Z – Perspiration

   (A) Y only (B) X and Y only
   (C) X and Z only (D) Y and Z only

72. Which of the following does not belong to the group formed by the others?

   (A) Snow leopards (B) Deer
   (C) Mountain goat (D) Yak

73. Which of the following food substances are protein rich food?

   (A) Rice
   (B) Brinjal
   (C) Organge
   (D) Groundnut

74. The functions of a vitamin are given below.

   – Prevents night blindness
   – Keeps skin healthy

   Which of the following vitamins is described inthe above information?

   (A) Vitamin A (B) Vitamin B
   (C) Vitamin C (D) Vitamin D

75. Which activity helps our body to produce vitamin D?

   (A) Jogging and exercising (B) Standing in the sun
   (C) Consuming more fruits (D) Practising Yoga

76. Ravi observed a swelling in his neck. What could be the disease he is suffering from?

   (A) Anaemia (B) Marasmus (C) Scurvy (D) Goitre

77. The diagram given below is the internal structure of an egg. Identify P, Q and R?

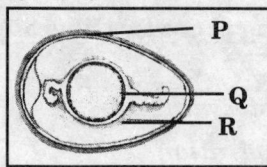

    (A) P – Egg shell, Q – Yolk, R – Albumen
    (B) P – Cell wall, Q – Albumen, R – Yolk
    (C) P – Cell membrane, Q – Albumen, R – Yolk
    (D) P – Egg shell, Q – Embryo, R – Albumen

78. Study the picture given below. Which of the following provides protection against scurvy?

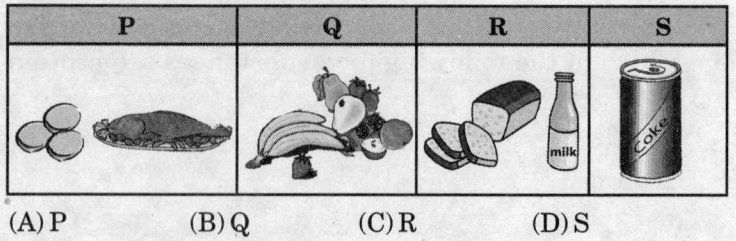

P	Q	R	S

    (A) P   (B) Q   (C) R   (D) S

79. Priya placed two drops of a liquid on some cooked rice, upon which the area covered by the liquid turned blue-black in colour. What could be the liquid?

    (A) Vegetable oil
    (B) Iodine solution
    (C) Benedict's solution
    (D) Nitrate solution

80. Which of the following is the correct sequence employed in making cotton fabrics?

    (A) Baling → Ginning → Spinning → Carding → Weaving
    (B) Ginning → Baling → Carding → Spinning → Weaving
    (C) Carding → Ginning → Baling → Weaving → Spinning
    (D) Carding → Ginning → Baling → Spinning → Weaving

81. A plant is placed in a box as shown in the diagram given below. The box is then placed in the garden.

   Which of the following changes you observe in the plant after two days?

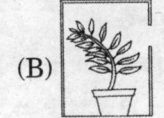

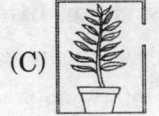

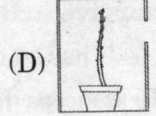

   (A) (B) (C) (D)

82. Which of the following represent I and II in the given chart?

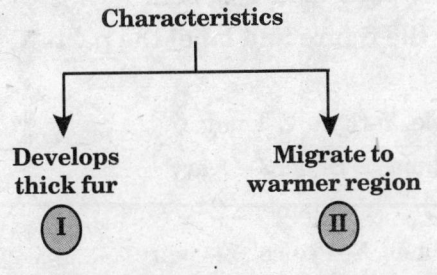

   Characteristics

   I: Develops thick fur
   II: Migrate to warmer region

   (A) I–Siberian crane, II–Penguin
   (B) I–Bear, II–Siberian crane
   (C) I–Penguin, II–Parrot
   (D) I–Duck, II–Penguin

83. Which of the following animals may represent 'X'?

   i. Rats
   ii. Chicken
   iii. Bears
   iv. Frogs

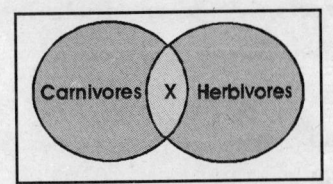

   Carnivores | X | Herbivores

   (A) i and iii only
   (B) iii and iv only
   (C) i, ii and iii only
   (D) i, ii, iii and iv

84. Study the characteristics of plants given below. Where do you find these plants?

   i. *Thick and fleshy stems*
   ii. *Leaves are modified into spines*
   iii. *Stems perform photosynthesis*

   (A) Plain areas (B) Mountain areas
   (C) Desert areas (D) Coastal areas

85. Which of the following adaptations help the camel to survive in desert conditions?

   (A) It has a layer of fat under its skin
   B) It sleeps during the day and is active at night
   C) It stores fat in its hump which can be broken down to water
   D) It stores water in its long neck

86. Observe the figure and label the parts X, Y and Z?

   (A) X–Style, Y–Style, Z–Ovule
   (B) X–Stigma, Y–Style, Z–Ovary
   (C) X–Anther, Y–Filament, Z–Ovary
   (D) X–Stamen, Y–Pedicel, Z–Ovary

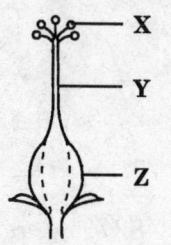

87. The structures labelled 'P' in the figure below are found in the internal part of the stem. What are the functions of 'P'?

   X – It transports food
   Y – It transports water and minerals
   Z – It gives shape to the stem

   (A) X and Y only
   (B) Y and Z only
   (C) X and Z only
   (D) X, Y and Z

88. Observe the diagram given below. Which two parts shown in the diagram work as a pair to move the bone that is attached to it?

   (A) R and Q
   (B) P and Q
   (C) P and R
   (D) S and Q

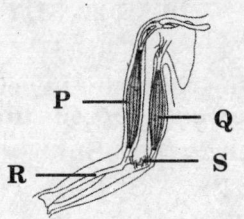

89. Read the features given below and identify the organism exhibiting these features.

   i. Steamlined body covered with scales

   ii. A swim bladder

   iii. Flexible vertebral column attached to muscles

   (A) Bird   (B) Earthworm
   (C) Snail   (D) Fish

90. Read the table and answer the question given below.

I	II	III
Sweet potato	Spinach	Potato
Radish	Cabbage	Onion
Beetroot	Lettuce	Turmeric

   Ginger can be placed in which of the following columns?
   (A) I   (B) III   (C) II   (D) I and II

CLASS: VI — GENERAL QUESTIONS

91. Which number should come next in the series given below?
    7, 10, 15, 22, 31, ?
    (A) 55   (B) 42   (C) 41   (D) 87

92. What is the missing character in between the letters given below, so that two words opposite to each other are formed?
    DOUB(?)LESS
    (A) M   (B) F   (C) P   (D) T

93. Which of the following instruments is used to observe celestial bodies?
    (A) Telescope   (B) Binoculars   (C) Microscope   (D) Anemometer

94. A hill is to mountain, as a stream is to:
    (A) avalanche   (B) canal   (C) glacier   (D) river

95. Which figure will come next in the series given below?

96. The computers of World Wide Web, which provide information or services to other computers are:
    (A) Web servers   (B) Web browsers
    (C) Web clients   (D) Web sites

97. The MacMohan line is between:
    (A) India and China   (B) India and Nepal
    (C) India and Pakistan (D) India and Myanmar

98. Who was the Vice President of India before B.S. Shekhawat?
    (A) Dr. Shankar Dayal Sharma   (B) K.R. Narayanan
    (C) K. Krishna Kanth   (D) R. Venkataraman

99. Which of the following countries is the venue of the summer olympic games to be held in 2008?
    (A) Sydney   (B) China   (C) India   (D) Japan

100. Pankaj Udhas, Britney Spears and Norah Jones together form a group of:
    (A) musicians   (B) singers   (C) film makers   (D) writers

CLASS : VI   NSTSE - 2011   MATHEMATICS

1. The whole numbers from 1 to 1000 are written. How many of these numbers have at least two 7's appearing side-by-side?
   (A) 10 (B) 11 (C) 21 (D) 19

2. In the diagram, the square has a perimeter of 48 cm and the triangle has a height of 48 cm. If the square and the triangle have the same area. What is the value of x?

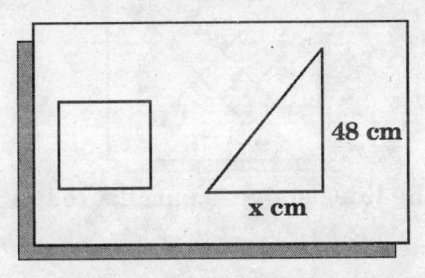

   (A) 1.5 cm (B) 12 cm (C) 6 cm (D) 3 cm

3. In the multiplication shown, P, Q and R are all different digits so that:

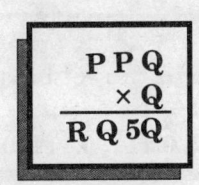

   $$\begin{array}{r} PPQ \\ \times\ Q \\ \hline RQ5Q \end{array}$$

   What is the value of P + Q + R?
   (A) 20 (B) 13 (C) 15 (D) 17

4. Mr. Z is a server at a restaurant. On Saturday Mr. Z gets up at 6 : 30 A.M., starts work at x A.M. and finishes at x P.M. How long does Mr. Z work on Saturday?
   (A) 24 − 2x hours (B) 12 − x hours
   (C) 2x hours (D) 12 hours

CLASS : VI Brain Mapping Academy

5 A fraction is equivalent to $\frac{5}{8}$. Its denominator and numerator add up to 91. What is the difference between the denominator and numerator of this fraction?

(A) 21   (B) 33   (C) 13   (D) 19

6

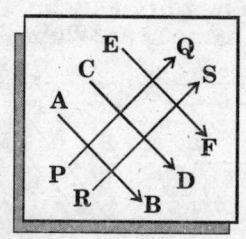

Which of the lines above is parallel to line PQ?

(A) AB   (B) CD   (C) EF   (D) RS

7 A movie theatre has eleven rows of seats. The rows are numbered from 1 to 11. Odd numbered rows have 15 seats and even-numbered rows have 16 seats. How many seats are there in the theatre?

(A) 176   (B) 186   (C) 165   (D) 170

8 The largest number in the set below is:

{0.109, 0.2, 0.111, 0.114, 0.17, 0.19}

(A) 0.109   (B) 0.2   (C) 0.114   (D) 0.19

9 The diagram shows a road map. Shyam drives to the post office and then to the petrol bunk.

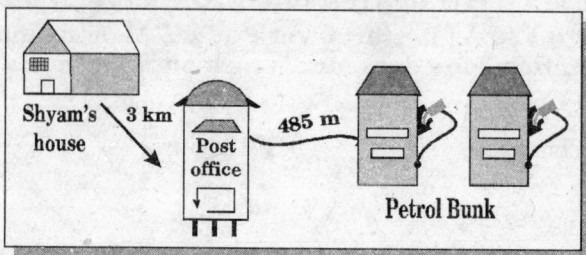

NSTSE - 2011

Find the distance, in km, driven by him?

(A) 3.485 (B) 5.15 (C) 4.885 (D) 7.85

10 Two positive integers have a sum of 11. The greatest possible product of these two positive integers is:

(A) 18 (B) 28 (C) 30 (D) 35

11 If P = 1000 and Q = 0.01, which of the following calculations give the largest result?

(A) P + Q (B) P × Q (C) $\dfrac{P}{Q}$ (D) $\dfrac{Q}{P}$

12 A parallelogram is shown below.

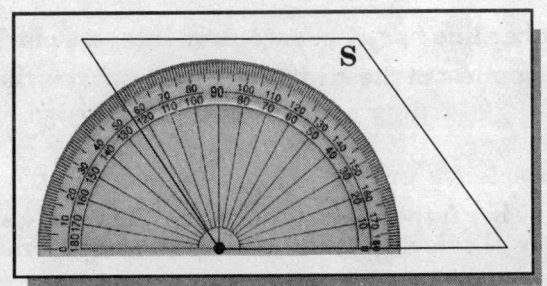

The measure of angle S to the nearest degree.

(A) 136° (B) 124° (C) 64° (D) 56°

13 If the ratio of boys to girls in the sixth-grade is 2 : 3, which of these shows possible number of the boys and girls in the class?

(A) 20 boys, 35 girls (B) 24 boys, 36 girls
(C) 35 boys, 20 girls (D) 36 boys, 24 girls

14 The ratio of the number of big dogs to the number of small dogs at a pet show is 3 : 17. There are 80 dogs, in total, at this pet show. How many big dogs are there?

(A) 12 (B) 20 (C) 24 (D) 6

15 Find the area of the shaded part in the figure below:

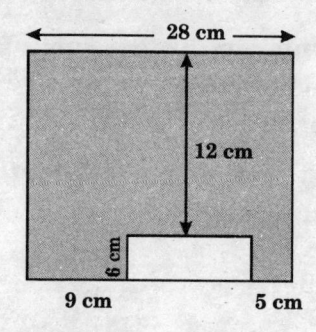

(A) 336 cm²   (B) 420 cm²   (C) 504 cm²   (D) 632 cm²

16 A number line has 40 consecutive integers marked on it. If the smallest of these integers is –11, what is the largest?

(A) 29   (B) 28   (C) 51   (D) 50

17 For a science project Ramya is keeping track of the calories her father eats at breakfast. The table shows the number of calories he ate at breakfast on Monday.

Breakfast Calories		
Food	Number of servings	Number of calories per serving
Oat cereal	1	80
Skim milk	1	40
Orange juice	1	86
Banana	1	105
Flavored coffee	1	55

Which is the closest to the number of calories Ramya's father ate at breakfast on Monday?

(A) 200 cal.   (B) 300 cal.   (C) 400 cal.   (D) 500 cal.

NSTSE - 2011

18 Each number in the sequence below has the same relationship to the number immediately before it.

$$24, 12, 6, 3, 1\tfrac{1}{2}$$

How can the next number in the sequence be found?

(A) By subtracting 12 from the previous number.

(B) By adding $1\tfrac{1}{2}$ to the previous number.

(C) By multiplying the previous number by 2.

(D) By dividing the previous number by 2.

19 The pictograph shows the bimonthly sale of bicycles of a store.

Duration	Bicycle sales in two months period
Nov. - Dec.	🚲🚲🚲🚲🚲
Sept. - Oct.	🚲
July - Aug.	🚲🚲🚲🚲
May - June	🚲🚲🚲
Mar. - Apr.	🚲

🚲 = 10 cycles

In what period were exactly 30 bicycles sold?

(A) July-August (B) May-June

(C) January-April (D) September-October

20 Lohith was asked to find 2 integers that have a difference of 1 and a sum of 59. He said the integers were 29 and 28. Why was Lohith's answer incorrect?

(A) The difference between 29 and 28 is not 1.

(B) The difference between 29 and 28 is 1.

(C) The sum of 29 and 28 is 59.

(D) The sum of 29 and 28 is not 59.

21. The diagram shows a triangle constructed with a piece of wire.

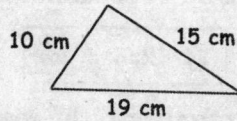

10 cm, 15 cm, 19 cm

Which of the following shapes can be constructed with the same piece of wire?

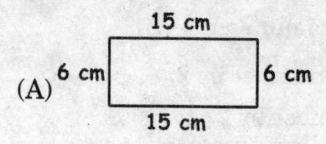

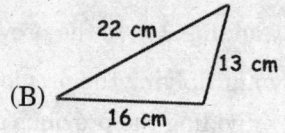

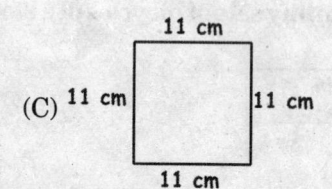

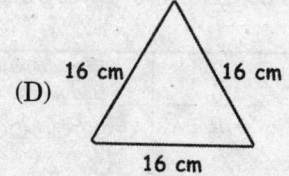

(A) Rectangle 15 cm × 6 cm

(B) Triangle 22 cm, 13 cm, 16 cm

(C) Square 11 cm × 11 cm

(D) Triangle 16 cm, 16 cm, 16 cm

22. What is the mixed number represented by 'X' below shown number line?

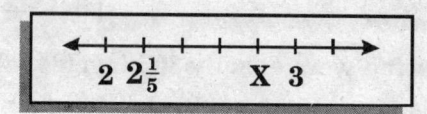

Number line: 2, $2\frac{1}{5}$, X, 3

(A) $2\frac{4}{5}$ (B) $2\frac{2}{5}$ (C) $2\frac{1}{2}$ (D) $2\frac{3}{4}$

23. PQRS is a straight line. PQ = 2 cm and PS = 40 cm. If PR : RS = 7 : 3, then QR in cm is:

(A) 12 (B) 10 (C) 26 (D) 28

24. A number is divided by three and multiplied by the square of a second number. The product is then divided by three. Write the algebraic term for the given statements using P as the first number and q as the second number.

(A) $9pq^2$ (B) $\frac{pq^2}{3}$ (C) $\frac{pq^2}{9}$ (D) $3pq^2$

NSTSE - 2011

25 Which of the following have maximum number of triangular faces?

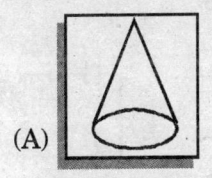

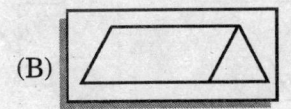

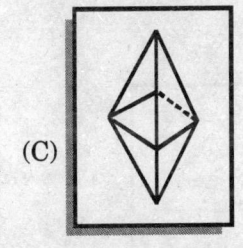

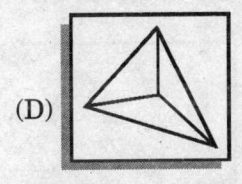

(A)

(B)

(C)

(D)

26. Identify the circuit diagram in which the bulb lights up.

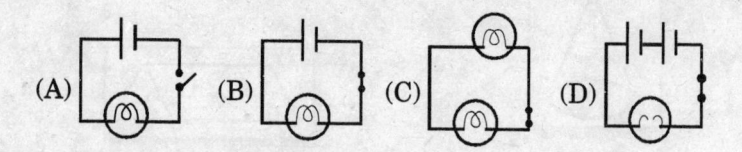

(A)   (B)   (C)   (D)

27. Look at the diagram given below:

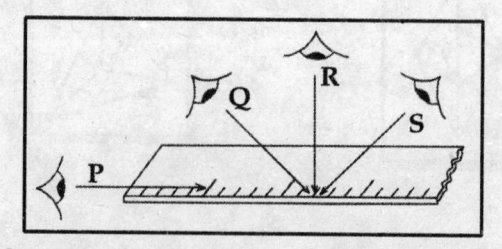

Which is the correct position to place the eye so that one can make the most accurate reading of the ruler?

(A) P (B) Q (C) R (D) S

28. Rahul observes a candle as shown in the figure below.

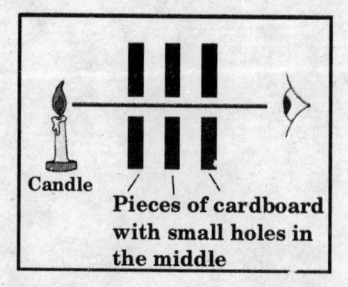

Candle   Pieces of cardboard with small holes in the middle

What inference can be made by Rahul from the given experiment?

NSTSE - 2011

(A) Light rays are very thin.

(B) Light rays travel in straight line.

(C) The eye can only see a luminous body.

(D) A beam of light is made up of lots of light rays.

29. Peter made a magnet using the "stroking" method as shown below:

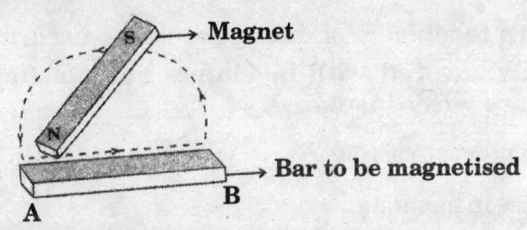

He started stroking the iron nail at A with a magnet and continued stroking in the direction shown. What poles does A and B represent?

	A	B
(A)	N-pole	S-pole
(B)	N-pole	N-pole
(C)	S-pole	N-pole
(D)	S-pole	S-pole

30. Look at the spinning of a top below:

What can be inferred about the motion of a spinning top?

(A) The top revolves about a fixed path with respect to time.

(B) The top exhibits a curvilinear motion under gravity.

(C) The top rotates about a fixed axis without changing its position with respect to time.

(D) The top moves to and fro about a fixed point.

31. Identify the *incorrect* statement from the following.

(A) Shadows always gives us the information about the shape of the object

(B) Images are different from shadows

(C) A plane mirror changes the direction of light that falls on it

(D) The moon is a non-luminous source of light

32. Somu's teacher explained that wires used in home are usually covered with insulators like plastic or rubber. Why are wires insulated?

(A) To prevent rusting

(B) Ease in handling

(C) Making the wire durable

(D) To prevent shock and short circuit

33. Which of the following objects *does not* need magnets to work?

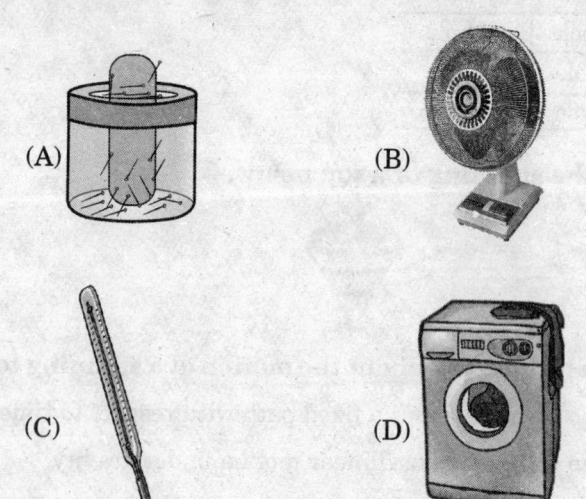

(A) (B) (C) (D)

34 Look at the arrangement of an experiment below.

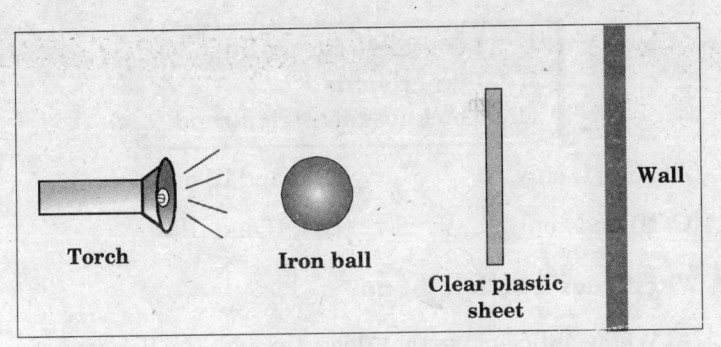

When the torch is switched on, we can observe shadow on the wall painted white. Which of the following correctly shows the shadow cast on the wall?

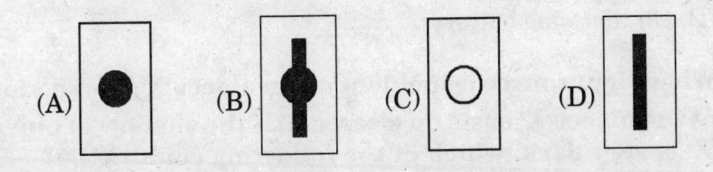

(A) ●   (B) ●with bar   (C) ○   (D) ▮

35 Look at the magnets given below.

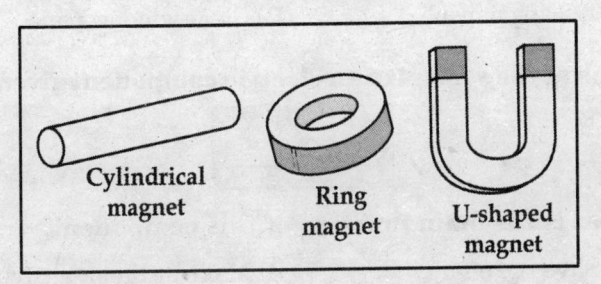

What do you infer ?

(A) All magnets are made of iron.

(B) The magnets are strongest at their poles.

(C) Like poles of magnets attract each other.

(D) Magnets can be made in different shapes and sizes.

36. Which of the following can be measured using a measuring tape?

> I. Length of a curved line
> II. Play grounds
> III. Thickness of a hair strand

(A) I and II only   (B) II and III only

(C) III and I only   (D) I, II and III

37. When does a bulb light up?

(A) When sufficient current flows through the filament.

(B) On heating the filament of the bulb.

(C) On exposing the bulb to a light source.

(D) On replacing battery.

38. When light source is incident on an object 'X', the shadow of the object 'X' casts on a screen. If the shadow of object 'X' is very dark, which of the following could 'X' be?

(A) Metal plate   (B) Glass

(C) Tracing paper   (D) Clear window pane

39. Look at the symbol of an electric component given below.

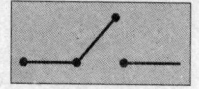

What is the main function of this component?

(A) Save the energy   (B) Make or break a circuit

(C) Prevent electric shocks (D) Make the bulb glow easily

40 Which of the following does NOT measure time?

(A) (B) (C) (D)

41 Which of the following ways *will not* make a magnet to lose its magnetism?

(A) Heat it strongly over a flame

(B) Drop it on the floor repeatedly

(C) Coat it with a layer of oil

(D) Hitting it with a hammer repeatedly

42 Why a non-luminous object is visible to us?

(A) It gives off visible light

(B) The light reflected by this object enters our eye

(C) It cannot be caught on a screen

(D) Light passes only in the form of rays

43 A circular disk with a stick moving about its axis through the centre is shown in figure below.

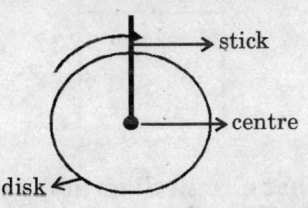

Identify the type of motion described by the stick.

(A) Rotatory motion (B) Circular motion

(C) Rectilinear motion (D) Oscillatory motion

44 Which of the following statements is *incorrect*?

(A) The closed path along which electric current flows is called a circuit.

(B) The bulb glows only when current flows through the circuit.

(C) An electric bulb is said to be fused if there is a break in its filament.

(D) Electrical wires are insulated with good conductors of electricity.

45 What fraction of a metre is 1 cm?

(A) Tens   (B) Hundreds (C) Tenth   (D) Hundredth

46 Anu did an experiment as shown in the figure below:

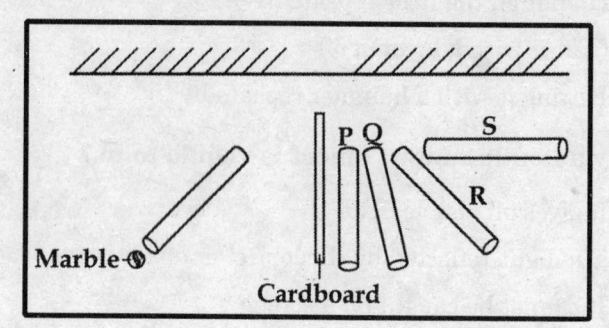

Which tube would enable Anu to see the marble?

(A) P   (B) Q   (C) R   (D) S

47 A teacher draws a circuit diagram (X) as given below:

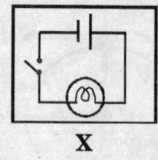

X

She explains that circuit diagram (X) uses symbols in an electric circuit? What does she mean by symbols?

(A) Cell   (B) Battery   (C) Bulb   (D) Components

48 Cubit, hand span and yard are three units of measurement of length.

Identify from the following the correct order of their increasing magnitudes.

(A) Hand span, yard, cubit (B) Hand span, cubit, yard

(C) Yard, cubit, hand span (D) Cubit, yard, handspan

49 Which of the following are luminous sources of light?

> I. Glow worm
> II. Star
> III. Metal spoon

(A) I and II only (B) II and III only

(C) III and I only (D) I, II and III

50 Which of the following is a bad conductor of electricity?

(A) Acid (B) Copper wire

(C) Distilled water (D) Human body

51. Look at the classification given below.

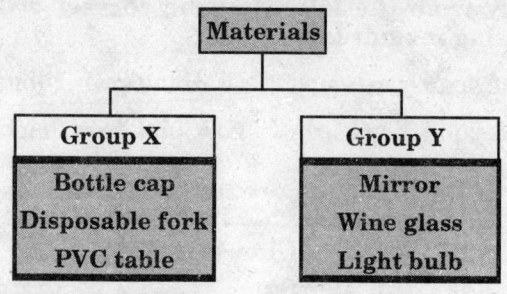

```
           Materials
          /         \
     Group X      Group Y
   Bottle cap     Mirror
   Disposable fork  Wine glass
   PVC table     Light bulb
```

Which of the following is correct?

	Group X	Group Y
(A)	Metal	Plastic
(B)	Plastic	Metal
(C)	Wood	Metal
(D)	Plastic	Glass

52. How are grain seeds removed from their stalks?

(A) Sieving (B) Winnowing
(C) Threshing (D) Any of the above

53. Anoop wants to select a material to make a hammock.

Which of the properties given below should he consider?
(A) Hard and water proof (B) Strong and flexible
(C) Transparent and water proof (D) Opaque and insulator

54 Identify an undesirable change from the following.

(A) Ripening of fruits.
(B) Occurrence of earthquakes.
(C) Preparing starch by photosynthesis in plants.
(D) Evaporation of sea water.

55 Look at Sunil in the figure given below.

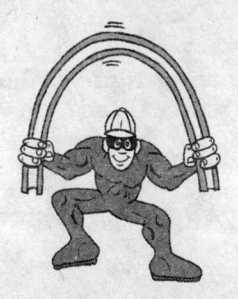

He bends a rod. Which property of the rod is responsible for him to bend the rod?
(A) Light in weight   (B) Hardness
(C) Water proof   (D) Flexibility

56 Sieving can be used only when the components of the mixture have :
(A) different sizes
(B) different melting points
(C) different boiling points
(D) different specific gravities

57 A needle and a knife belong to the same group because :
(A) they are transparent
(B) they are hard and magnetic
(C) they float on water
(D) they are poor conductors of heat

58 A flask filled partially with water is shown below.

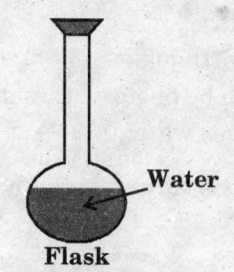

Which of the following figures shows the correct water level in the flask when tilted?

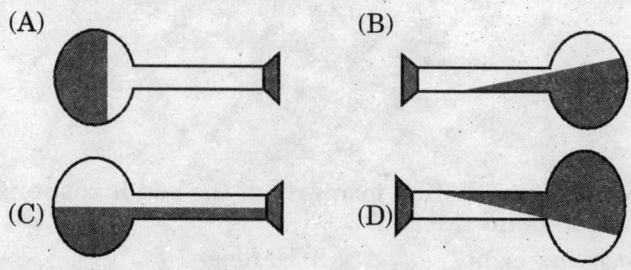

(A) (B) (C) (D)

59 A few coloured glass pieces that are big in size are mixed with sugar. Which is the easiest way to separate them?
(A) Heat the mixture   (B) Add the mixture to water
(C) Handpick the glass pieces (D) Handpick the sugar particles

60 What kind of change is the making of a ring from pure gold ?
(A) Irreversible chemical change
(B) Irreversible physical change
(C) Reversible chemical change
(D) Reversible physical change

61 Dheeraj covered the mouths of three bowls with three sheets made of different materials X, Y and Z. He then poured a table spoon of cooking oil onto the sheet. The results are as shown in the diagram below.

Which material absorbs oil the least?
(A) X (B) Y (C) Z (D) Cannot be said

62. In a cloud, the size of the droplets increases causing rainfall because:
(A) they become heavier
(B) they become lighter
(C) they convert into steam
(D) of reflection of light

63. What is the process we use to separate a mixture of water and sulphur?
(A) Filtration
(B) Sublimation
(C) Evaporation
(D) Distillation

64. Identify the chemical change from the following.
(A) Heating of sugar.
(B) Dissolution of sugar in water.
(C) Crystallisation of sugar.
(D) Powdering of sugar.

65. Which of the following methods of separation needs air for its separation?
(A) Hand picking
(B) Sieving
(C) Winnowing
(D) Filtration

66. What is a homogeneous mixture?
(A) It is made up of only elements
(B) It contains only compounds
(C) It is a liquid-liquid mixture
(D) It is that in which constituents can't be distinguished

67. Milk curdles when lemon juice is added. What is this?
(A) Evaporation
(B) Coagulation
(C) Reversible change
(D) Photochemical change

68 Rohit went to a shop to buy a towel to wipe after a bath. He saw towels made up of cotton, polyester, nylon and wool. Which one of these towels will he buy as the first preference?

(A) Cotton   (B) Polyester   (C) Nylon   (D) Wool

69 Shilpa sprinkles water in a dirty room before sweeping. Why?

(A) Sprinkling water is fashionable
(B) Sweeping of water is easier
(C) Water coagulates the dust particles
(D) Water repels dust particles

70 How is air pollution on the roads reduced?

(A) Widening the roads
(B) Having more traffic lights on the roads
(C) Having less traffic lights on the roads
(D) Reducing the number of vehicles on the road

71 Read the information given below.

> P : Supplies materials for building cells
> Q : Supplies a lot of energy
> R : Supplies high dietary fibre

Which of the following food combinations is correct according to the definitions of P,Q and R?

	P	Q	R
(A)	Fish	Lettuce	Sunflower oil
(B)	Beans	Butter	Potato
(C)	Meat	Butter	Whole grains
(D)	Potato	Fish	Butter

72 How does the camel's hump help the camel to survive in the desert?

(A) It helps the camel to balance its body while walking on sandy ground

(B) It stores food which can provide the camel with energy during food shortage

(C) It protects the camel during sandstorms

(D) It helps the camel to get protection from the enemies

73 Frogs are amphibians. They live both on land and in water. Which of the following adaptations enable the frogs to live both on land and in water?

I. They have gills that help them to breathe in the water
II. Their skin, when kept moist, can intake oxygen dissolved in water
III. They have lungs that help them to breathe when they are on land
IV. They can trap air bubbles in their throat

(A) I and III only (B) I and IV only
(C) II and III only (D) II and IV only

74 Which of the following groups consists of a herbivore, a carnivore and an omnivore respectively?

(A) Giraffe, House lizard, Rat
(B) Toadstool, Goat, Eagle
(C) Mould, Bear, Snake
(D) Giraffe, Rat, Vulture

75 Observe the two leaves given below.

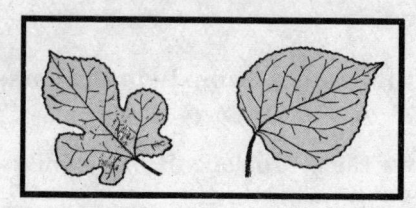

They are similar because:

(A) they have the same venation
(B) they have the same edges
(C) their shapes are the same
(D) their plants have different kinds of roots

76 Sandy is allergic to manmade fabric, so she only wears clothes made of natural fibre. Which one of the following materials will you recommend her not to use?

(A) Nylon   (B) Wool
(C) Cotton (D) Silk

77 Abhi added a few drops of a liquid on a slice of potato, upon which the area covered by the liquid turned blue black in colour. What could be the liquid?

(A) Benedict's solution   (B) Dilute iodine solution
(C) Tollen's reagent   (D) Concentrated nitric acid

78 Given below are two groups of materials used to make clothing.

Cotton	Fur
Jute	Leather
Flax	Silk

On what basis these have been grouped?

(A) Air space inside fibres   (B) Air space between fibres
(C) Water absorption   (D) The basis of their sources

79 Which of the following features are useful for desert plants?

I. Water storing stems
II. Leaf hairs
III. Large flat leaves
IV. Needle like leaves

(A) II and IV only   (B) I and III only
(C) I and IV only   (D) III and IV only

80 Study the diagram given below carefully. It shows the relationship between photosynthesis and respiration. Which arrows is/are wrong?

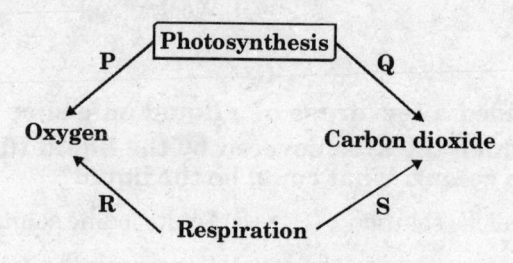

```
        P   ┌──────────────┐   Q
         ↙  │Photosynthesis│  ↘
            └──────────────┘
    Oxygen                    Carbon dioxide
         ↖      R       S   ↗
              Respiration
```

(A) P only (B) Q only
(C) R and S only (D) Q and R only

81 Look at the diagram below carefully.

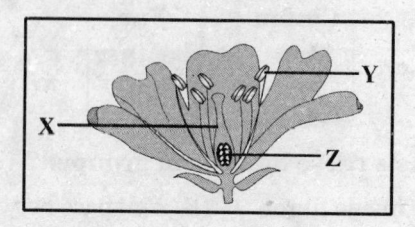

Which of the following represents X, Y and Z?

	X	Y	Z
(A)	Anther	Filament	Ovule
(B)	Style	Stigma	Ovary
(C)	Style	Anther	Ovary
(D)	Filament	Style	Ovary

NSTSE - 2011

82 Study the classification chart given below.

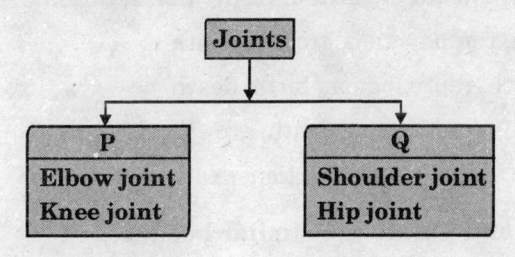

```
              Joints
            /        \
           P          Q
      Elbow joint   Shoulder joint
      Knee joint    Hip joint
```

What are P and Q?

	P	Q
(A)	Gliding joint	Pivot joint
(B)	Hinge joint	Ball and socket joint
(C)	Pivot joint	Hinge joint
(D)	Hinge joint	Gliding joint

83 Which food items from the given choices should be included in our diet to protect us from bleeding gums?

(A) Cheese (B) Yeast (C) Amla (D) Wheat germ

84 Identify the material 'P' from the information given below.

P
Can be recycled
Bio-degradable
Non-toxic and useful

(A) Paper   (B) Glass bottle
(C) Metal can   (D) Plastic bottle

85 Which of the following options comprises various stages in the life of an organism in proper sequence?

(A) birth, reproduction, growth, death

(B) growth, reproduction, birth, death

(C) birth, reproduction, death, growth

(D) birth, growth, reproduction, death

86 Ginger and potato are similar because:

(A) both are modified tap roots (B) both are modified stems

(C) both are modified fibrous roots (D) both are fruits

87 Observe the diagram given below.

Which of the following characteristics can be proved through this experiment?

> I.   The shoot of the plant bends towards sunlight.
> II. The given plant requires oxygen for respiration.
> III. The given plant needs sunlight to make food.

(A) I only   (B) I and II only

(C) I and III only   (D) I, II and III

88 Compressing of raw cotton in bundles is called:
(A) baling (B) spinning
(C) weaving (D) rafting

89 Which of the following joints works as the figure given below?

(A) Ankle and knee joints
(B) Hip and shoulder joints
(C) Neck and wrist joints
(D) Shoulder and knee joints

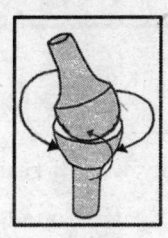

90 Based on characteristics given in the box, identify the plant.

> I. Grow in marshy areas
> II. Breathing roots grow out of the soil

(A) Hydrilla (B) Mangroove
(C) Banyan (D) Duckweed

CLASS : VI — GENERAL QUESTIONS

91. Complete the given series:

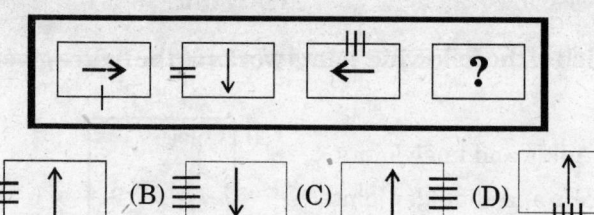

(A) (B) (C) (D)

92. The country which ranks second in land area is:

(A) China   (B) Canada   (C) India   (D) Australia

93. Meteorolgy deals with:

(A) Weather   (B) Meteors   (C) Metals   (D) Earthquakes

94. Which of the following is nearest in meaning to the word '**cachet**'?

(A) An automobile   (B) A seal
(C) A frame work   (D) A shrill cry

95. Who has become the first woman President of India?

(A) Mira Nair   (B) Sarojini Naidu
(C) Indira Gandhi   (D) Prathibha Devisingh Patil

96. Who developed the World Wide Web?

(A) Timothy Bernes Lee   (B) Jim Osborne
(C) Gordon Moore   (D) James Watt

97. Which of the following Indian monuments received UNESCO World Heritage status on 30 November 2007?

(A) Golconda Fort   (B) Charminar
(C) Red fort   (D) Taj Mahal

98. Today is Thursday. What will be the 25th day from today?
   (A) Saturday (B) Tuesday
   (C) Wednesday (D) Monday

99. Madam Curie, Alfred Nobel and C.V. Raman are all eminent Scientists in the branch of :
   (A) Botany (B) Chemistry
   (C) Physics (D) Zoology

100. At present the number of zones in Indian Railways is/are:
   (A) Seventeen (B) Nine
   (C) Twelve (D) Sixteen

KEY FOR THE MODEL PAPER – 1

1. B	2. C	3. B	4. D	5. C	6. C	7. B	8. D	9. A	10. A
11. D	12. A	13. D	14. B	15. D	16. A	17. B	18. C	19. B	20. B
21. D	22. C	23. A	24. C	25. B	26. A	27. B	28. B	29. D	30. C
31. B	32. D	33. C	34. A	35. A	36. B	37. C	38. B	39. D	40. C
41. D	42. C	43. B	44. B	45. A	46. C	47. A	48. B	49. C	50. D
51. B	52. B	53. A	54. B	55. D	56. B	57. C	58. A	59. B	60. B
61. B	62. B	63. B	64. A	65. D	66. B	67. B	68. C	69. D	70. A
71. D	72. C	73. C	74. B	75. C	76. C	77. C	78. D	79. B	80. C
81. C	82. B	83. B	84. D	85. D	86. C	87. C	88. C	89. B	90. D
91. C	92. D	93. C	94. A	95. A	96. B	97. B	98. D	99. A	100. C

KEY FOR THE MODEL PAPER – 2

1. C	2. D	3. B	4. A	5. C	6. B	7. D	8. C	9. B	10. C
11. B	12. B	13. C	14. A	15. D	16. A	17. D	18. C	19. B	20. A
21. C	22. C	23. B	24. C	25. D	26. B	27. C	28. D	29. D	30. A
31. D	32. D	33. D	34. B	35. A	36. C	37. B	38. D	39. C	40. B
41. C	42. B	43. B	44. A	45. C	46. B	47. C	48. D	49. C	50. B
51. B	52. A	53. B	54. D	55. B	56. D	57. B	58. B	59. C	60. B
61. A	62. C	63. D	64. A	65. D	66. B	67. C	68. B	69. C	70. B
71. B	72. C	73. C	74. B	75. C	76. C	77. B	78. D	79. B	80. C
81. D	82. D	83. C	84. D	85. A	86. C	87. C	88. C	89. B	90. C
91. B	92. C	93. B	94. C	95. D	96. B	97. C	98. C	99. B	100. D

KEY FOR THE MODEL PAPER – 3

1. C	2. B	3. C	4. D	5. B	6. A	7. B	8. C	9. D	10. D
11. A	12. B	13. B	14. A	15. B	16. A	17. C	18. D	19. C	20. A
21. D	22. A	23. D	24. C	25. C	26. C	27. B	28. B	29. B	30. B
31. A	32. D	33. D	34. B	35. C	36. D	37. C	38. D	39. C	40. B
41. B	42. D	43. D	44. A	45. B	46. D	47. B	48. B	49. B	50. C
51. B	52. D	53. A	54. C	55. D	56. C	57. B	58. B	59. C	60. A
61. D	62. C	63. A	64. A	65. C	66. B	67. B	68. C	69. D	70. B
71. A	72. B	73. D	74. A	75. B	76. D	77. A	78. B	79. B	80. B
81. A	82. B	83. C	84. C	85. C	86. B	87. B	88. B	89. B	90. B
91. B	92. D	93. A	94. D	95. C	96. A	97. A	98. C	99. B	100. B

KEY FOR THE Q.P. - 2011

1. D	2. C	3. D	4. D	5. A	6. D	7. D	8. B	9. A	10. C
11. C	12. B	13. B	14. A	15. B	16. B	17. C	18. D	19. B	20. D
21. C	22. A	23. C	24. C	25. D	26. B	27. C	28. B	29. A	30. C
31. A	32. D	33. C	34. A	35. D	36. A	37. A	38. A	39. B	40. D
41. C	42. B	43. A	44. D	45. D	46. C	47. D	48. B	49. A	50. C
51. D	52. C	53. B	54. B	55. D	56. A	57. B	58. C	59. B	60. D
61. C	62. A	63. A	64. D	65. C	66. C	67. B	68. A	69. C	70. D
71. C	72. B	73. C	74. A	75. A	76. A	77. B	78. D	79. C	80. D
81. C	82. B	83. C	84. A	85. D	86. A	87. A	88. A	89. B	90. B
91. C	92. B	93. A	94. B	95. D	96. A	97. C	98. D	99. C	100. A